Preface

Foundation Skills–Chemistry *is a series of three volumes which give the ideal introduction to Chemistry for the 11–14 age group. I hope, looking at this book, you have already benefited from Volumes 1 and 2. Chemistry is an important subject which all pupils should study up to the age of 14 if not beyond. It may be taught either as a separate subject or as a part of a Science course. That is just a matter of school organization and in no way alters the content of the subject. For many careers a physical science qualification is essential at 16+. The key to this success is to establish firm foundations and that is what* Foundation Skills–Chemistry *seeks to do.*

The methods of teaching Chemistry have changed dramatically in the past decade. No longer is it sufficient to learn a large number of facts and reproduce them on the examination paper. Parents who find it difficult to understand the work of their children will, I hope, enjoy the new approach working alongside the child.

Emphasis is now given to the acquisition of specific skills and mastering of different concepts. These cannot just be learned but must be developed. The pupil will be introduced to the required skills and concepts at the correct level of maturity.

These books provide, in addition to a clear exposition of basic chemical information, a large number of activities which will help to develop a pupil's basic skills. Some of these activities are practical and can be carried out safely at home using items that are readily available. These activities are shown with an asterisk. Adult supervision in these practical activities is strongly advisable, especially in activities involving electricity: batteries should always be used, never mains electricity. Other activities involve the use of practical information in various forms. Some activities are comprehension exercises and others are left deliberately open to stimulate the pupil's imagination.

I have had great pleasure from hearing of successes of students who have used my book *Revise Chemistry* for O Level or CSE. I am sure success can be made more certain by the correct early groundwork in the subject.

The *Foundation Skills–Chemistry* series has required considerable research and discussion. I thank Roy Williams in particular for all his work in connection with the development of this project. My two sons, Robin and Timothy, have been most helpful having just gone through the study of Chemistry in school from the pupil's side!

I must thank the staff of Charles Letts and Co Ltd for their help in the production of the series, especially Pat Rowlinson and Anne Henwood.

Finally, and certainly not least, I must thank my wife Judy for all her patience and help as this project has developed.

G. R. McDuell 1986

4

Contents

Introduction

and guide to using the book

You will find that the Chemistry topics met by a student between the ages of 11 and 14 are covered in the three volumes of Foundation Skills – Chemistry. The approach of every teacher will be different and so the order of topics might be different.

In general terms, Volume 1 is aimed at 11–12 year olds or anyone starting Chemistry.

Volume 2 is aimed at 12–13 year olds.

Volume 3 is aimed at 13–14 year olds.

In Volume 1, the first steps in Chemistry are taken with emphasis given to aspects of safety and chemical 'vocabulary'. This is further developed in Volume 2 but there are the first introductions to some difficult abstract concepts which can cause problems if not mastered at a later stage.

Volume 3 is designed to give a realistic view of Chemistry. The ideas of symbols, formulae, equations and chemical calculations which can cause such problems are introduced. The reasons for studying Chemistry in the upper school to 16+ examination level are also explained. Often 'option choices' are made without sufficient understanding of the relevance of particular subjects.

Much research has been done in recent years into methods of learning and much discussion has been directed at deciding what should constitute a Chemistry course up to 16+. The Assessment of Performance Unit (APU) was set up in 1975 as a branch of the Department of Education and Science (DES). The Unit aims to provide information about the levels of performance pupils achieve in different subjects and how their performance changes over the years.

The terms of reference of the APU are: 'To promote the development of methods of assessing and monitoring the achievement of children at school, and to seek to identify the incidence of under-achievement'.

To this end, in Science, the APU, based at Chelsea College, University of London, and at the University of Leeds, has carried out a large number of tests of pupils aged 11, 13 and 15. The analysis of the results of these tests has enabled the researchers to identify the levels of understanding which we can expect pupils to have at different ages. Foundation Skills – Chemistry, in its three volumes, follows the direction shown by the APU.

The Examination Boards have jointly produced 16+ recommended National Criteria for Chemistry which provide guidelines for new examinations in Chemistry at 16+. Foundation Skills – Chemistry takes account of National Criteria in Chemistry.

I am sure parents, teachers and pupils are aware of the importance of supporting work done in school by planned work at home. Present financial restrictions prevent schools buying books for pupils to take home to read. Foundation Skills – Chemistry provides a complete home back-up to work done in school. Success at 16+ very much depends upon firm foundations set at an early stage.

On pages 8–9 there is a skills, concepts and topic analysis table which is a most valuable part of the series. Down the left-hand side of page 8 are listed the various topic units in the book (i.e. contents). Across the top of pages 8 and 9 the various skills and concepts are shown – one column for each. An analysis has been made to show which skills and which concepts are used in each topic unit. The symbol ● means that the particular skill or concept will be needed for that topic unit.

You will notice if you look in all three volumes that the complete range of skills and concepts will not be covered unless the full course is followed. This is because there is a right stage for the introduction of each concept or for the development of a particular skill.

The pupil should work through the topic units in the same order as they are taught in his or her school. Throughout the three volumes the left-hand pages consist of vital information necessary to introduce the different topics. On the facing right-hand pages are the 'Activities' so vital for developing skills and mastering concepts.

Having read through a particular topic unit the pupil should attempt the appropriate 'Activities' section. The 'Activities' are not designed as examination questions. They are intended to practise skills and extend understanding of difficult concepts. They should also be interesting and not too much like homework. When the 'Activities' have been tried the pupil can then compare his or her answers with the answers at the back of each book. At the back of each book there is also a glossary of chemical terms which the pupil can refer to at any time.

The essential skills identified as important for Chemistry up to 14 and beyond are:

1 Representation by symbols
  A Reading information from
    I diagrams
    II graphs
    III tables and charts
    IV classification keys and flow diagrams
    V chemical formulae and equations
  B Representing information as
    I diagrams
    II graphs
    III tables and charts
    IV classification keys and flow diagrams
    V chemical formulae and equations

2 Using apparatus and measuring instruments
  A The correct piece or pieces of apparatus for a particular purpose
  B Accurate measurement

3 Observation
  A Making accurate observations
  B Interpreting observations

4 Interpreting and application
  A Interpreting presented information
  B Selecting the most suitable statement from a series of statements
  C Applying a concept to the understanding of new information
  D Making generalizations from information

5 Designing investigations
  A Identifying or suggesting statements which can be tested
  B Planning parts of an investigation
  C Planning a whole investigation

6 Carrying out investigations. This skill is difficult to practise without laboratory equipment and supervision.

The following concepts are identified as relevant:
  1 Safety
  2 Accuracy and limitations on accuracy
  3 Mixing and dissolving
  4 Separation
  5 Purity
  6 Change
  7 States of matter and their interconversion
  8 Acidity and alkalinity
  9 Elements
  10 Combination
  11 Competition
  12 Oxidation and reduction
  13 Analysis
  14 Particulate nature of matter
  15 Movement of particles
  16 Arrangement of particles (structure)
  17 Atomic structure
  18 The mole, chemical formulae and nomenclature
  19 Economic considerations
  20 Energy

Chemical engineer at work

Chemist at work in laboratory

SKILLS

Topic Units

Groups: **1 REPRESENTATION** (AI–BV) · **2 USING APPARATUS** (A, B) · **3 OBSERVATION** (A, B) · **4 INTERPRETING and APPLICATION** (A, B, C, D) · **5 DESIGNING INVESTIGATIONS** (A, B, C) · **6 PRACTICAL**

Topic Units	AI	AII	AIII	AIV	AV	BI	BII	BIII	BIV	BV	2A	2B	3A	3B	4A	4B	4C	4D	5A	5B	5C	6
1 Water	●		●								●				●		●			●		
2 Solubility and solubility curves	●	●	●			●	●				●			●	●					●		●
3 Solubility of gases in water	●		●			●		●		●	●		●	●	●		●	●		●	●	
4 Water supply						●		●							●							
5 Hard and soft water	●		●		●		●	●			●	●	●	●	●	●	●	●		●		●
6 Detergents	●												●	●	●					●	●	●
7 Water pollution	●		●		●							●	●	●		●						
8 Crystals and water of crystallization											●		●	●	●	●						●
9 The effects of the atmosphere on chemicals											●		●	●	●		●		●			
10 Atoms and their structure	●							●							●							
11 Ions and electrolysis	●		●			●		●						●	●							
12 The Periodic Table	●		●			●		●					●	●	●			●				
13 The alkali metals	●						●									●	●					
14 The halogens														●	●		●					
15 The noble gases			●							●				●			●				●	
16 Carbon														●			●					
17 Silicon													●	●	●		●					
18 The transition metals	●							●					●	●	●		●		●			
19 Chemical formulae			●					●		●												
20 Chemical equations				●						●					●		●					
21 Salts	●			●		●		●			●				●	●				●		
22 Petroleum																						
23 Coal					●					●			●	●	●		●			●		

Key

1 A Reading information from
  I   diagrams
  II graphs
  III tables and charts
  IV classification keys and flow diagrams
  V   chemical formulae and equations

B Representing information from
  I   diagrams
  II graphs
  III tables and charts
  IV classification keys and flow diagrams
  V   chemical formulae and equations

2 Using apparatus and measuring instruments
  A The correct piece or pieces of apparatus for a purpose
  B Accurate measurement

3 Observation
  A Making accurate observations
  B Interpreting observations

4 Interpreting and application
  A Interpreting presented information
  B Selecting the most suitable statement from a series of statements
  C Applying a concept to the understanding of new information
  D Making generalizations

5 Designing investigations
  A Identifying or suggesting statements which can be tested
  B Planning parts of an investigation
  C Planning a whole investigation

6 Carrying out investigations

CONCEPTS

1	2	3	4	5	6	7	8	9	10	11	12	13	14	15	16	17	18	19	20		
				●	●	●		●	●										●	Water	1
●	●	●	●		●															Solubility and solubility curves	2
		●	●		●	●	●											●		Solubility of gases in water	3
●			●	●		●					●							●		Water supply	4
	●	●		●	●		●											●		Hard and soft water	5
		●	●	●	●													●		Detergents	6
																				Water pollution	7
		●		●	●								●	●						Crystals and water of crystallization	8
		●			●															The effects of the atmosphere on chemicals	9
								●					●	●		●				Atoms and their structure	10
			●		●															Ions and electrolysis	11
								●			●		●			●				The Periodic Table	12
●					●		●	●			●									The alkali metals	13
					●		●	●	●		●									The halogens	14
			●	●	●	●		●	●				●		●					The noble gases	15
●								●			●				●			●	●	Carbon	16
					●			●	●	●	●								●	Silicon	17
					●			●												The transition metals	18
					●			●	●				●				●			Chemical formulae	19
					●	●											●			Chemical equations	20
	●		●		●		●										●			Salts	21
●			●	●	●	●												●	●	Petroleum	22
●	●															●		●	●	Coal	23

Key

1 Safety
2 Accuracy and limitations of accuracy
3 Mixing and dissolving
4 Separation
5 Purity
6 Change
7 States of matter and their interconversion
8 Acid and alkalinity
9 Elements
10 Combination

11 Competition
12 Oxidation and reduction
13 Analysis
14 Particulate nature of matter
15 Movement of particles
16 Arrangement of particles
17 Atomic structure
18 The mole, chemical formulae and nomenclature
19 Economic considerations
20 Energy

Why choose Chemistry?

In your third year you will probably be asked to choose subjects to study in the fourth and fifth years leading to General Certificate of Secondary Education (GCSE). The subjects you choose will affect the choice of subjects you might make in the sixth form or at college and the career you can follow later in life. A great deal of thought should be given to this choice.

In the fourth and fifth years you will certainly have to study Mathematics and English. Beyond these subjects the curriculum will vary very much from school to school. You should try to get a 'balance' of subjects to leave your choices open as long as possible. You should certainly study a Science subject (e.g. Chemistry, Physics or Biology), a Humanities subject (e.g. Geography, History or Religious Education), a practical subject (e.g. Craft, Design and Technology, Home Economics, Art, Music or Technology) and a foreign language, if possible.

For many careers a GCSE (or O grade in Scotland) Chemistry qualification is needed or preferable. In many cases you will need to study Chemistry beyond the age of sixteen taking GCE A level (or Higher in Scotland). This section is intended to give you some ideas of why Chemistry should be studied in the upper school.

farmer

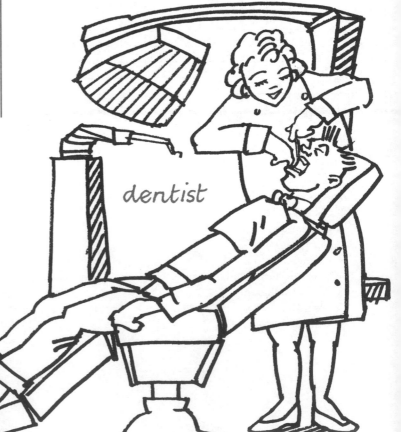

dentist

pharmacologist

Fig. 1 Jobs leading from Chemistry

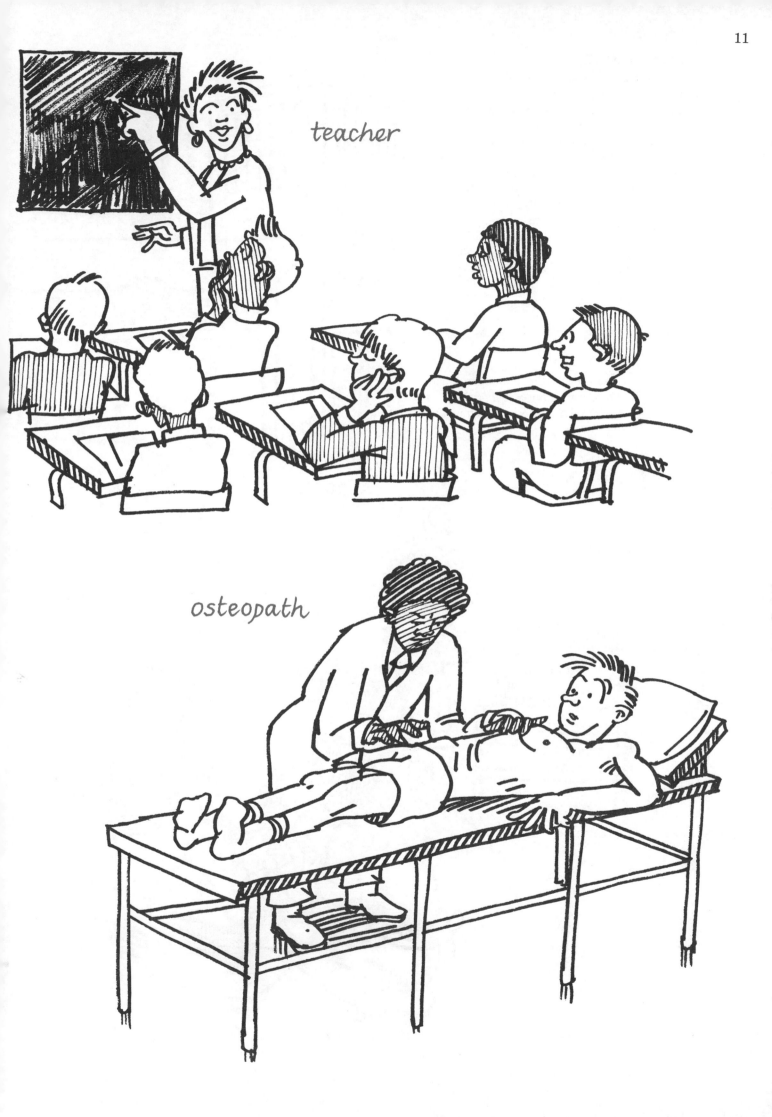

teacher

osteopath

What is Chemistry?

Chemistry is the science of the material world. It is concerned with the structure and interactions of all the matter in the universe—whether animal, vegetable or mineral.

It stands in a central position among the basic sciences—Physics, Chemistry and Biology. On the one hand it is linked with Physics through Physical Chemistry and on the other with Biology through Biochemistry. Life depends basically on chemical reactions. Chemistry is therefore fundamental to Physiology and to Medicine. It plays an important part in the development of such sciences as Geology and it underlies many branches of technology such as Atomic Energy, Metallurgy, Fuel Technology and particularly Chemical Engineering.

Fig. 1 shows some of the jobs that you might follow after studying Chemistry. Some of these jobs you can start at sixteen and others you have to enter later after further study.

If you require further information about careers in Chemistry you should contact your careers teacher or The Royal Society of Chemistry, 30 Russell Square, London WC1B 5DT.

factory inspector

nurse

chiropodist

Fig. 1 Jobs leading from Chemistry

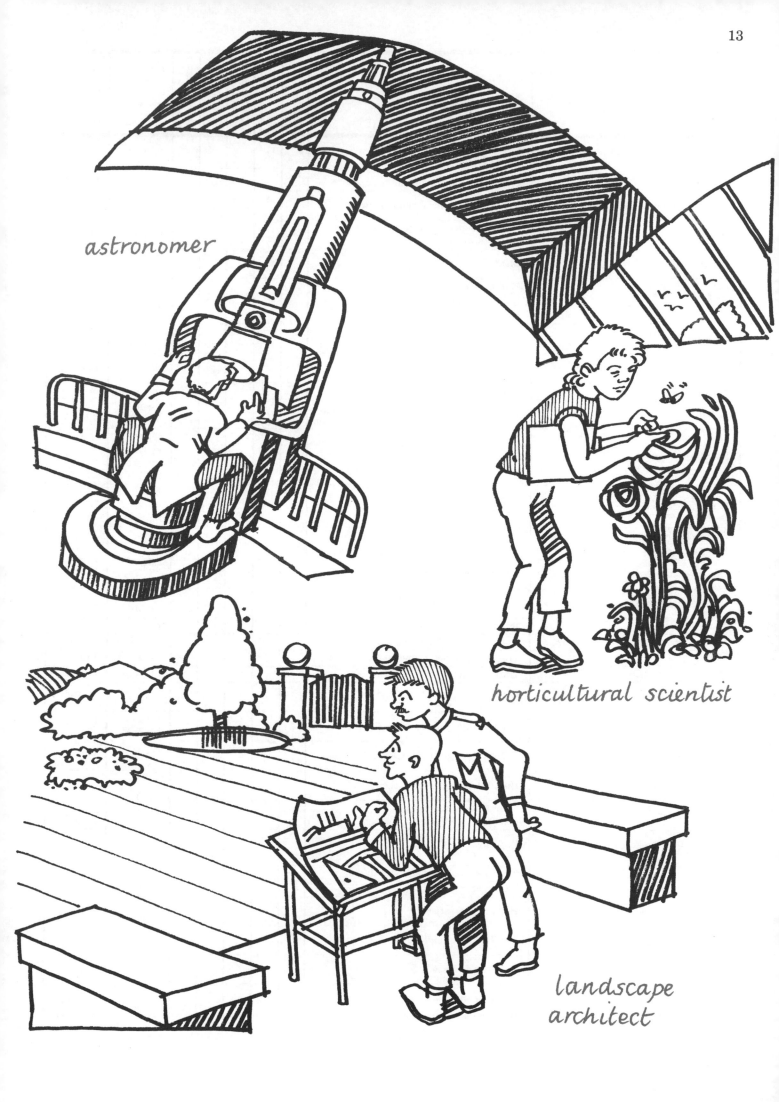

astronomer

horticultural scientist

landscape architect

14

Job	Brief summary of the job	Study beyond 16	GCSE Chemistry needed	GCSE Chemistry preferred	A level Chemistry needed	A level Chemistry preferred	Other GCSE subjects needed (see key)	Other A Levels needed (see key)
Animal technician	Looking after animals in research laboratories		√				inc M, E	
Biochemist	Chemistry of plant and animal tissue	√	√		√		range	B, P or M
Chemical engineer	Large scale chemical manufacture	√	√		√		range inc E	M
Chemist	Study of composition and properties of substances	√	√		√		range	M, P
Dental hygienist	Cleaning and polishing teeth for dentist		√				range inc E, B	
Dental technician	Making dentures			*			P	
Dentist	Diagnosis and treatment of mouth disorders	√	√		√		range	B, P or M
Dietician	Advising on diet	√	√		√		range inc M, P, E	B
Doctor	Prevention, diagnosis and treatment of illness	√	√		√		range	B, P
Farm manager	Running a farm	√	√			√	range	M
Fish farmer	Breeding and rearing fish OR	√	√ / √			√	range inc M, E	B
Food technologist	Processing, storage and distribution of food OR	√	√	√	√		range inc M, E / range inc B, M, E	B
Forensic scientist	Examining material from the scene of crime OR	√		√ / √			E, M / range inc E, M	B
Fuel technologist	Preparation and supply of fuels	√	√		√		range	B
Home economist	Advising consumers and manufacturers	√	√		√		M, E	
Leather technologist	Making, treating and dyeing leather OR	√		* / √			M, E / range	P, M or B
Market garden manager	Running a market garden	√	√		√		range inc M	B
Materials scientist	Studying glass, plastic etc	√	√		√		range	P or M
Medical laboratory scientific officer	Applying science to prevent disease	√	√		√		P, M, B	M, B or P
Metallurgist	Treatment of metals and alloys	√	√		√		range	P, M
Microbiologist	Working with microorganisms	√	√		√		range	B
Minerals surveyor	Surveys for mining	√	√		√		range inc E & M	M, P
Pharmacist	Supply drugs and medicines to the public	√	√		√		range inc E, M	P, B
Pharmacologist	Effects of drugs on animals and humans	√	√		√		range inc E, M	P, B
Pharmacy technician	Hospital or shop helping chemist			*			at least 3 subjects	
Polymer technologist	Manufacture and testing of plastics and rubber OR	√	√	√	√		M, E	P, M
Printing technologist	Printing OR	√	√	√		√	M, E	
Public analyst	Ensuring public safety by analysis	√	√		√		range	P, M
Quality control technician	Testing to ensure quality			√			M, E	
Science laboratory technician	Helping a scientist	√	√	√			M, E range	P or B
Textile technologist	Testing fabrics and yarns	√		√ / √		√	M, E, B	
Timber technologist	Treatment of wood products	√	√	√		√	M, E	P, M
Veterinary surgeon	Treating animals	√	√		√		range inc M, E	P, B

Table 1 Academic requirements for careers involving Chemistry

Key: √ GCSE Grade A, B, C   * GCSE Grade D, E, F   M Mathematics P Physics   B Biology E English, inc including

Choosing your job

Table 1 lists some of the jobs where Chemistry is required or is preferable. The information in the table is only intended as a guide. You may find you can enter the same job at different ages and with different qualifications.

In addition Chemistry is a most useful qualification for entering the following jobs:

agricultural scientist
archaeologist
astronomer
biologist
chiropodist
civil engineer
conservation officer (museum)
electrical/electronic engineer
environmental health officer
environmental engineer
factory inspector
farmer
forester
geneticist
geologist
geophysicist
horticultural scientist
jeweller
landscape architect
mechanical engineer
medical physicist
meteorologist
nurse
ophthalmic optician
osteopath
pest controller
physiologist
physicist
physiotherapist
psychologist
photographer
printer
radiographer
teacher of Biology
teacher of Chemistry
teacher of Home Economics
teacher of Mathematics
teacher of Physics
technical sales representative
technical writer

In addition to all these Chemistry is a useful subject which shows an employer that you can study a subject in depth, understand some scientific principles and consider some abstract concepts.

More and more students are leaving Further Education colleges. Students may be attending to follow a CPVE (Certificate of Pre-Vocational Education) course or as part of a YTS (Youth Training Scheme) programme. The courses at these colleges are more vocational than at school i.e. they are more closely linked to a job. Chemistry is a valuable subject as an introduction for many further education courses. Hairdressing and catering are examples of courses with considerable Chemistry content.

Going further in Chemistry

Table 2 lists the degree courses which require A-level Chemistry. Unlike some subjects, Chemistry is a subject which is very difficult to start at A level, as so much depends upon building up an understanding during the GCSE course.

Agriculture	Genetics
Agricultural sciences	Geochemistry
Agricultural bacteriology	Geology
Agricultural biochemistry	Glass technology
Agricultural botany	Human biology
Agricultural chemistry	Human ecology
Agricultural zoology	Human sciences
Analytical chemistry	Inorganic chemistry
Animal biology	Materials science
Animal nutrition	Material technology
Animal physiology	Marine biology
Animal sciences	Marine botany
Applied biochemistry	Marine zoology
Applied biology	Medical biochemistry
Applied electrochemistry	Medicine
Bacteriology	Metallurgy
Biochemical engineering	Microbiology
Biochemistry	Mineral exploitation
Biological chemistry	Mineral sciences and technology
Biology	Minerology
Biological sciences	Molecular sciences
Biomedical electronics	Natural sciences
Biomedical engineering	Neurobiology
Botany	Nutrition
Brewing	Oil technology
Cell biology	Paper science
Ceramics	Pathology
Chemical education	Petrology
Chemical engineering	Pharmaceutical chemistry
Chemical physics	Pharmacology
Chemical process	Pharmacy
Chemical technology	Physical chemistry
Chemistry	Physical sciences
Colour chemistry	Physiology
Colour technology	Plant sciences
Crystallography	Polymer chemistry
Dentistry	Polymer and colour science
Development physiology	Polymer engineering
Dietetics	Polymer sciences and technology
Dyeing and dyestuffs technology	Science (general)
Forestry	Science (history and philosophy of)
Earth sciences	Soil science
Environmental sciences	Textile technology
Exploration science	Theoretical chemistry
Farm animals (physiology and biochemistry of)	Veterinary science
Fibre science	Virology
Food science and technology	Wood science
Forestry	Zoology
Fuel science	

Table 2 Courses requiring A-level Chemistry

I hope having read this section, and thought very carefully about it, you will seriously consider studying Chemistry at least up to the age of sixteen.

Unit 1

Water

Water has featured in various units in Foundation Skills – Chemistry *Volumes 1 and 2. In this unit various facts about water are gathered together. You should know all of this at the start of the third year.*

1.1 States of water

The three states of water are: ice – solid; water – liquid; steam – gas. 0°C is the freezing point of pure water and the melting point of pure ice. 100°C is the boiling point of pure water.

Impurities dissolved in water lower the freezing point and increase the boiling point of the water.

1.2 Testing for water

Water is a colourless liquid with no smell. It is a neutral liquid, i.e. it has a pH of 7. There are, however, other neutral and colourless liquids that have no smell.

Anhydrous copper(II) sulphate is a white powder formed when blue copper(II) sulphate crystals are heated (Volume 1 Unit 19). When a liquid which contains water is added to anhydrous copper(II) sulphate, the powder turns blue and gets hot.

Also, cobalt(II) chloride paper, which is a piece of filter paper dipped in cobalt(II) chloride solution and dried, is pale blue in colour. When a piece of cobalt(II) chloride paper is dipped into water, or a liquid containing water, the paper turns pink.

The best test for pure water is to carry out melting and boiling point tests. Only pure water boils at 100°C (at normal atmospheric pressure) and freezes at 0°C.

1.3 Reactions of metals with water

In *Foundation Skills – Chemistry* Volume 2 Unit 5 reactions of metals with water were discussed. Potassium, sodium and calcium react readily with cold water to produce an alkali solution and hydrogen gas.

potassium + water → potassium hydroxide + hydrogen

sodium + water → sodium hydroxide + hydrogen

calcium + water → calcium hydroxide + hydrogen

Magnesium hardly reacts with cold water but reacts rapidly with steam.

magnesium + steam → magnesium oxide + hydrogen

Similarly, zinc and iron can react with steam.

1.4 Electrolysis of water

Water can be split up with reactive metals such as potassium, sodium and calcium (Unit 1.3). Alternatively, water can be split up by using electricity in a process called electrolysis.

Pure water does not conduct electricity well and it is usual to add a little dilute sulphuric acid to the water before electrolysis. This does not alter the products but speeds up the process.

Fig. 1.2 shows a piece of apparatus called Hofmann's voltameter being used for the electrolysis of acidified water. A colourless gas is produced at the positive electrode (anode) and a different colourless gas is produced at the negative electrode (cathode). These two gases collect in the vertical tubes.

1.5 Synthesis of water

Water is formed as a product in many chemical reactions. When a jet of hydrogen gas burns in oxygen (or air) water is produced.

hydrogen + oxygen → water

This reaction can be very dangerous to do because mixtures of hydrogen and air can explode.

Fig. 1.1 Tony will never again taste a liquid to see if it's water

Activities

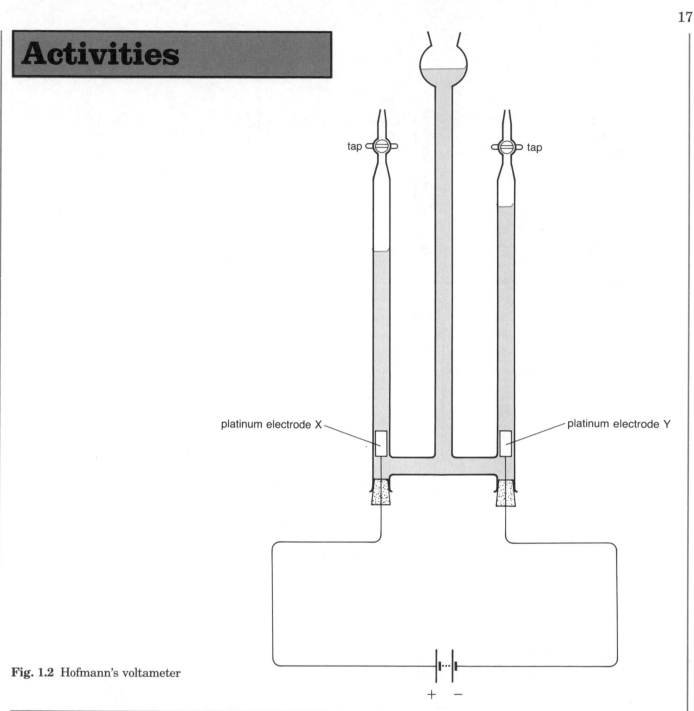

tap

tap

platinum electrode X

platinum electrode Y

+ −

Fig. 1.2 Hofmann's voltameter

Test	Liquid A	B	C
Boiling point °C	100	68	103
With anhydrous copper(II) sulphate	white to blue	no change	white to blue
With cobalt(II) chloride paper		no change	blue to pink
Evaporate to dryness	no residue	no residue	white residue
pH		7	7

Table 1.1

1 Table 1.1 contains information about three substances A, B and C.

(a) Complete the information in the table.

(b) Which liquid A, B or C:
   (i) is pure water;
   (ii) is an aqueous solution;
   (iii) contains no water?

2 Fig. 1.3 shows four arrangements for finding the boiling point of a colourless liquid.

(a) Which arrangement, A, B, C or D, would be most suitable for finding the boiling point of the colourless liquid?

(b) Why would these arrangements be unsuitable for finding the boiling point of a flammable liquid?

3 Fig. 1.4 shows pieces of laboratory apparatus.

(a) Name each piece of apparatus in Fig. 1.4.

(b) Draw a labelled diagram of apparatus set up to produce some pure water from a sample of impure water containing dissolved impurities.
(Do not draw stands, bosses and clamps used to support the apparatus.) In addition to the apparatus in Fig. 1.4 you will need a Bunsen burner and corks.

(c) What is the name given to the experiment being carried out in your diagram?

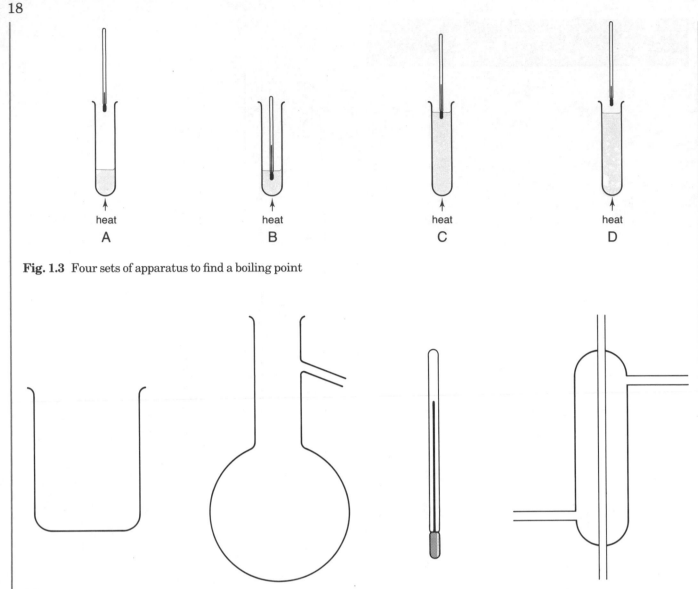

Fig. 1.3 Four sets of apparatus to find a boiling point

A   B   C   D

heat   heat   heat   heat

Fig. 1.4 Pieces of apparatus

August Wilhelm von Hofmann (1818–1892)

Hofmann was born in Giessen in Western Germany on 8 April 1818. He first studied law and philosophy at Geissen University before studying Chemistry as Assistant to Justus von Liebig.

When the Royal College of Chemistry was founded in 1845 he accepted the invitation to become its first director. He was recommended for the post by Liebig. Many chemists who later became famous were trained there by him. In 1856 he became Chemist to the Royal Mint.

In 1865 he returned to Berlin as Professor of Chemistry and remained there until his death.

In 1868 he founded the German Chemical Society and was, for many years, its President. The headquarters of this society was named Hofmann Haus in his memory.

His research interests were many with special interest in organic chemistry, particularly synthetic dyes and organic bases (including aniline), called amines.

During his lifetime nearly 1000 articles or books were produced by his laboratory. Of these nearly 300 were his original work.

He was able to deliver lectures in four languages and also wrote books about chemical history.

He was a brilliant teacher conveying tremendous enthusiasm. He brought about tremendous changes in Chemistry teaching and showed the importance of demonstrating experiments during lectures. An example of his demonstrations is Hofmann's voltameter which is a piece of apparatus he devised to demonstrate electrolysis. He was himself rather clumsy and usually entrusted the demonstrations to more skilled assistants.

4 Answer the following questions about the above passage.

(a) How old was Hofmann when:
  (i) he became Director of the Royal College of Chemistry;
  (ii) he returned to Berlin;
  (iii) he died?

(b) Explain the meaning of the following terms in the passage:
  (i) organic chemistry;
  (ii) synthetic;
  (iii) base.

(c) It has been said that Hofmann was 'the greatest influence on the development of Chemistry in the nineteenth century'.

List any evidence in the passage to support this statement.

5 The following questions refer to the electrolysis of water in Fig. 1.2.

(a) Which electrode, X or Y, is the anode (positive electrode)?

(b) Which electrode, X or Y, is the cathode (negative electrode)?

(c) The gas collected in the right hand tube burns with a squeaky pop. What is this gas?

(d) The gas collected in the left hand tube relights a glowing splint. What is this gas?

(e) Which gas is produced more quickly? (Both tubes were full of water at the start of the experiment.)

(f) If the taps are opened the water levels in the tubes rise and the gases escape rapidly. Why do the water levels rise?

Summary

Water is a neutral liquid with no smell or taste. Pure water boils at 100°C (at normal pressure) and freezes at 0°C.

A liquid containing water turns anhydrous copper(II) sulphate from white to blue. It will also turn cobalt(II) chloride paper from blue to pink.

Water is split up by electrolysis into hydrogen and oxygen.

Unit 2

Solubility and solubility curves

Water is a very good solvent in which a wide range of solutes dissolve.
Solubility is a quantitative concept. This means that it describes **how much**, i.e. what mass, of a solute will dissolve in a fixed mass of solvent (usually water). Solubility also changes with temperature and the temperature always has to be given.
The solubility of a solute X in water is defined as the maximum mass of X, in grams, which will dissolve in 100 g of water at a particular temperature.

2.1 The solubility of sodium chloride at room temperature

A beaker is half filled with water at room temperature. Sodium chloride (salt) is added to the water in small portions. After each addition, the solution is stirred. Sodium chloride is added until no more sodium chloride will dissolve and some remains undissolved. This is called a **saturated** solution.

A dry evaporating basin is weighed and some of the solution, without sodium chloride crystals, is poured into the evaporating basin which is then weighed again.

The solution is carefully evaporated to dryness. After cooling, the evaporating basin is weighed again. The process is summarized in Fig. 2.1.

Sample results

1   Mass of evaporating basin = 50.25 g
2   Mass of evaporating basin + sodium chloride solution = 118.25 g
3   Mass of evaporating basin + solid sodium chloride = 68.25 g

From these results

Mass of sodium chloride solution = **2 − 1**
$$= 118.25 \text{ g} - 50.25 \text{ g}$$
$$= 68.00 \text{ g}$$

Mass of solid sodium chloride   = **3 − 1**
$$= 68.25 \text{ g} - 50.25 \text{ g}$$
$$= 18.00 \text{ g}$$

Mass of water in solution   = **3 − 2**
$$= 118.25 \text{ g} - 68.25 \text{ g}$$
$$= 50.00 \text{ g}$$

18.00 g of sodium chloride dissolved in 50.00 g of water at room temperature.

$$\therefore \frac{18}{50} \times 100 \text{ g of sodium chloride dissolved in 100 g of}$$

water at room temperature.

The solubility of sodium chloride at room temperature is 36.0 g per 100 g of water.

The experiment could be repeated preparing saturated solutions of sodium chloride at different temperatures and then evaporating samples of these solutions to dryness. This would give solubilities of sodium chloride at different temperatures but would be a time-consuming exercise.

Fig. 2.1 Experiment to find the solubility of sodium chloride

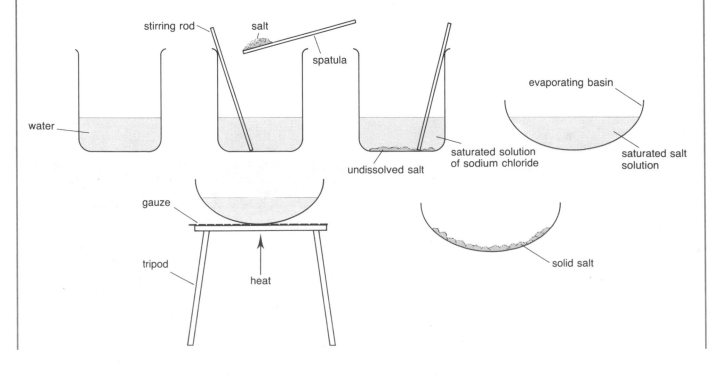

2.2 The solubility of potassium chlorate at different temperatures

A weighed amount of potassium chlorate is put into a dry test tube. A measured volume of water is added to the test tube and the test tube is heated until all of the solid potassium chlorate has dissolved. The test tube is then allowed to cool and the solution is constantly stirred with a thermometer. The temperature is noted when crystals first start to appear.

A known volume of water is added to the test tube and the test tube reheated and cooled as before. A new temperature is recorded.

If this is repeated, a series of volumes of water and temperatures are recorded. Sample results are shown in Table 2.1 for an experiment using 2.0 g of potassium chlorate.

2.3 Solubility curves

A solubility curve is a graph of the solubility of a solute (on the vertical or y axis) against temperature (on the horizontal or x axis). It shows clearly the way that the solubility of the solute changes with temperature.

The results in Table 2.1 are shown in the graph in Fig. 2.2. Note that the points are joined together with a smooth curve.

From the solubility curve in Fig. 2.2 it can clearly be seen that the solubility of potassium chlorate increases as temperature increases. This is true for most solid solutes in water and can be expressed simply as:

Solid solutes become more soluble in water as temperature rises.

Total volume of water (cm^3)	Total mass of water (g)	Temperature at which crystals are first seen (°C)	Solubility (calculated) (g per 100 g of water) $\dfrac{\text{mass potassium chlorate} \times 100}{\text{mass of water}}$
4	4	90	$\frac{2}{4} \times 100 = 50.0$
6	6	74	$\frac{2}{6} \times 100 = 33.3$
8	8	62	$\frac{2}{8} \times 100 = 25.0$
12	12	48	$\frac{2}{12} \times 100 = 16.7$
16	16	36	$\frac{2}{16} \times 100 = 12.5$
20	20	27	$\frac{2}{20} \times 100 = 10.0$

Table 2.1 Solubility at different temperatures

NB The mass of 1 cm^3 of water is 1 g

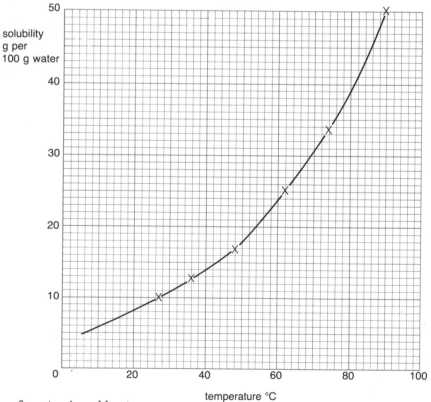

Fig. 2.2 Solubility curve for potassium chlorate

Activities

*1 A supersaturated solution

A supersaturated solution is one that contains more of the solute in the solution than it should. You can make a supersaturated solution of 'hypo' (sodium thiosulphate crystals, available from a photographic shop) or Glauber's salt (sodium sulphate crystals available from a chemist).

Put about 3 cm depth of water into a test tube and then add three teaspoonfuls of either 'hypo' or Glauber's salt. Heat the test tube gently until the crystals dissolve. Cool the test tube by running it under the water from the cold tap. Do not move the test tube at this stage. You will find that no crystals form even though there is far more solute present than will dissolve in the small mass of water.

If a small crystal of 'hypo' or Glauber's salt is added the whole solution will immediately crystallize. The same will happen if the solution is stirred.

Why is it important to stir the solution continuously in the experiment to find the solubility of potassium chlorate at different temperatures?

2 Jill and Peter carried out experiments to find the solubility of sodium chloride at room temperature (Unit 2.1). Their results are shown in Table 2.2.

(a) Calculate, from their results in Table 2.2, the solubility of sodium chloride at room temperature obtained by Jill and Peter. The correct result is 36.0 g per 100 g of water.

Which of them obtained a result closest to the correct result?

	Peter's results	Jill's results
Mass of evaporating basin	65.32 g	67.55 g
Mass of evaporating basin + salt solution	125.32 g	137.55 g
Mass of evaporating basin + salt	75.32 g	87.55 g

Table 2.2 Peter's and Jill's results

(b) Peter thought his result was inaccurate because he lost too much salt during the evaporation by spitting.

He decided to repeat the experiment but this time he evaporated the solution on a water bath (Fig. 2.3). List any mistakes in the apparatus set up in Fig. 2.3. Draw a section diagram of the apparatus set up correctly for this evaporation on a water bath. What must Peter do to the evaporating basin before carrying out the final weighing?

Apart from using a water bath, what could Peter do to reduce the spitting of salt during evaporation?

(c) Jill decided that her result was different from the correct result because her sodium chloride was not completely dried after evaporation.

She repeated the experiment and obtained the following results.

Mass of evaporating basin	= 67.55 g
Mass of evaporating basin + salt solution	= 145.55 g
Mass of evaporating basin + salt after evaporation	= 88.55 g

At this point she reheated the evaporating basin for five minutes, allowed it to cool and then re-weighed it. The mass was now 88.55 g. What could she conclude from these results?

3 List all of the apparatus required in order to carry out the experiment to find the solubility of potassium chlorate at different temperatures (Unit 2.3).

4 Fig. 2.4 shows solubility curves for the following solutes: sodium chloride, potassium nitrate, copper(II) sulphate. Use this graph to answer the following questions.

(a) Which one of these substances
  (i) has almost the same solubility at all temperatures;
  (ii) is least soluble at 0°C;
  (iii) is most soluble at 60°C?

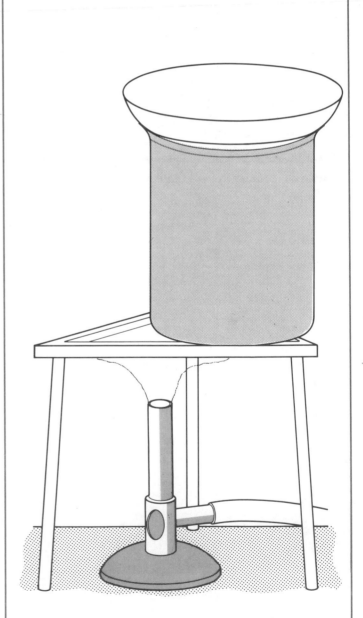

Fig. 2.3 Peter's water bath to evaporate the solution

23

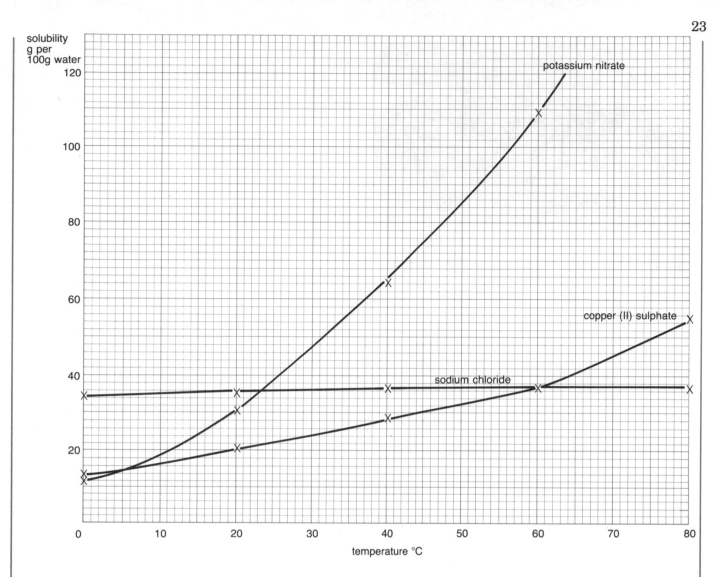

Fig. 2.4 Solubility curves

(b) From Fig. 2.4 find:

  (i) the solubility of potassium nitrate at 30°C;

  (ii) the temperature at which the solubility of copper(II) sulphate is 24 g per 100 g of water;

  (iii) the maximum number of grams of copper(II) sulphate which will dissolve in 50 g of water at 70°C;

  (iv) the temperature at which the solubility of potassium nitrate and sodium chloride is the same.

(c) Table 2.3 gives the solubility of ammonium chloride in water at different temperatures.
Plot these results on the graph in Fig. 2.4.

Temperature °C	0	10	20	40	60	80
Solubility (g per 100 g water)	30	33	37	46	55	66

Table 2.3 Solubility of ammonium chloride at different temperatures

Summary

The solubility of a solute X in water is defined as the maximum mass of X, in grams, which will dissolve in 100 g of water at a particular temperature. Most solid solutes increase in solubility as temperature rises. For this reason a solution is often heated to speed up the dissolving process.

A graph showing the solubility of a solute at different temperatures is called a solubility curve.

Unit 3

Solubility of gases in water

In Unit 2 it was seen that many solids are quite soluble in water and the solubility of solid solutes in water usually increases with a rise in temperature.

Most gases are much less soluble in water. We usually describe their solubility by the volume of a gas which dissolves in a given volume of water at a particular temperature. Table 3.1 gives the volume of some common gases in cm^3 which will dissolve in 1 dm^3 ($1000cm^3$) of water at different temperatures.

From these results we can make the following conclusions.

1 Gases are less soluble than solid solutes.
2 The solubility of a gas decreases with increasing temperature.
3 Ammonia and hydrogen chloride are much more soluble in water than other gases.
4 When a gas dissolves well in water it reacts with the water to form either an acid or an alkaline solution.

3.1 The fountain experiment

The fountain experiment is used to demonstrate the solubility of ammonia or hydrogen chloride.

A dry round bottom flask is filled with either dry ammonia or hydrogen chloride. The apparatus is set up as in Fig. 3.1.

When a little air is blown into the apparatus, the water rises from the lower flask to the upper flask. The gas in the upper flask readily dissolves in the water and more water enters the upper flask to fill the space. A fountain is seen coming from the tube in the upper flask.

3.2 Getting the dissolved air from a water sample

Air which is dissolved in water at room temperature will not dissolve when the temperature of the water is raised.

The apparatus in Fig. 3.2 is set up with the whole apparatus filled with tap water. The flask is then heated until the water starts to boil. The gas which was dissolved in water at room temperature collects in the graduated tube over water.

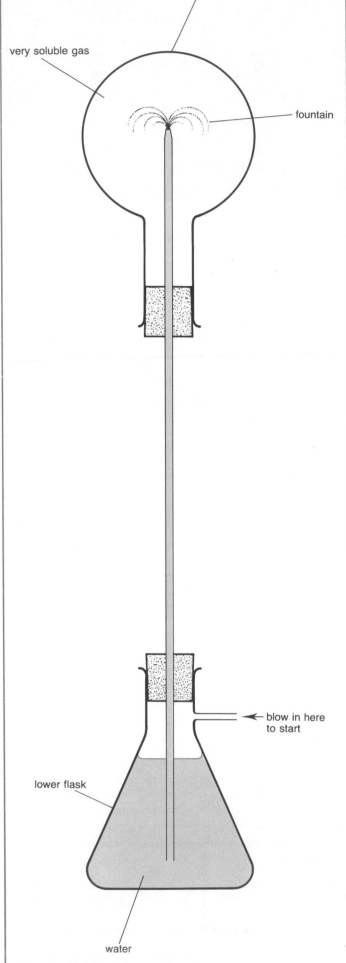

Fig. 3.1 The fountain experiment

3.3 Importance of dissolved gases

Water normally contains only a very small percentage of dissolved air. This air contains oxygen which provides the oxygen required by fish in a river or pond. A fish takes in water through its mouth, removes the oxygen and lets the water out through its gills. Because there is little oxygen in water, the fish has to take in a large volume of water to get the oxygen that it needs.

Green plants in water can 'oxygenate' water by putting oxygen back into water. If water is polluted by the addition of chemicals, the oxygen in the water decreases and the fish die (see Unit 7).

Dissolved air in water causes rusting on the inside of radiators and iron pipes. Rusting requires the presence of oxygen and water (see *Foundation Skills – Chemistry* Volume 1 Unit 21). From time to time air which has escaped from the water on heating collects inside the radiator and has to be released.

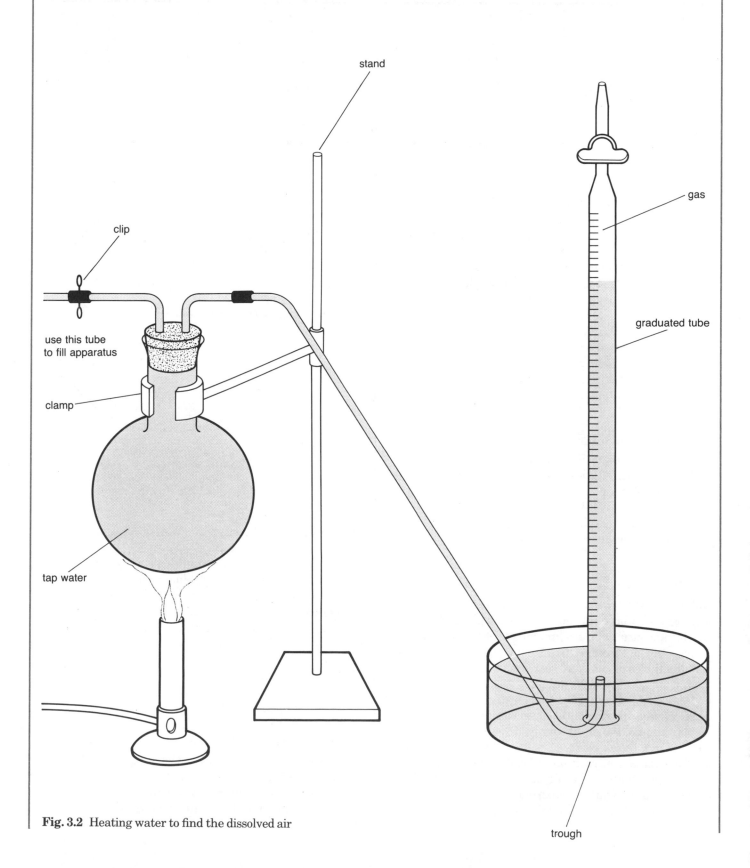

Fig. 3.2 Heating water to find the dissolved air

Activities

1 Answer the following questions using the
information in Table 3.1.

Gas	Formula	Temperature (°C)			pH of resulting solution
		10	20	30	
Ammonia	NH_3	870 000	680 000	530 000	10
Argon	Ar	41	32	28	7
Carbon dioxide	CO_2	1 160	848	652	5
Chlorine	Cl_2	3 090	2 260	1 770	1
Hydrogen	H_2	19	18	17	7
Hydrogen chloride	HCl	475 000	442 000	412 000	1
Nitrogen	N_2	18	15	13	7
Oxygen	O_2	37	30	26	7
Sulphur dioxide	SO_2	56 600	39 400	27 200	2

Table 3.1 Solubility of common gases in water

(a) Using this information only, decide which of the
following statements are true and which are false.
   (i) Only ammonia dissolves in water to form an
alkaline solution.
   (ii) A solution of carbon dioxide in water is more
strongly acidic than a solution of sulphur dioxide.
   (iii) Six of the gases in the table are elements.
   (iv) All of the compounds in the table dissolve
more easily than the elements.
(b) What volume of ammonia would dissolve in 100
cm^3 of water at room temperature (20°C)?
(c) List the gases in the table which dissolve in water
to form acid solutions.

*2 Looking at a bottle of 'pop'

A bottle of lemonade or a similar drink is made by
bubbling carbon dioxide under pressure through a
flavoured solution.
   Carefully remove the top from a bottle of 'pop'.
Observe the change which occurs to the solution.
Explain the observation that you have made.

3 Heating water

John carried out an experiment to heat up a beaker of
water and observe the changes taking place. When
the temperature of the water was about 25°C the
outside of the beaker started to mist up. At about 65°C
small bubbles of gas were seen escaping from the
water. At 100°C violent bubbling was seen.
   Draw a table giving the temperature at which the
observation was made, the observation and an
explanation of the observation.

4 In *Foundation Skills – Chemistry* Volume 1 Unit
20 the normal composition of air was given. Fig. 3.3
gives a 'pie' diagram for the normal composition of air.
   Jenny carried out an experiment to find the
composition of air dissolved in a sample of water
(Unit 3.2).

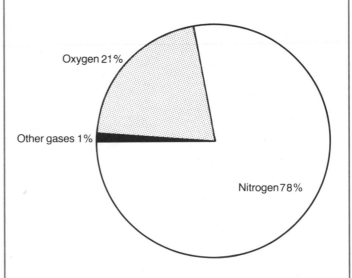

Fig. 3.3 Pie diagram showing the composition of normal air

(a) Draw a labelled section diagram of the apparatus
that she used (see Fig. 3.2).
(b) Joan, passing by, asked Jenny if she was allowing
for the steam that is being produced when the water is
boiled and is collected in the graduated tube. What
answer would you give to Joan?
(c) Describe briefly an experiment that Jenny could
use to find the percentage of oxygen in the air she
collected.
(d) From her results she found the following
composition:

   Oxygen 35%
   Nitrogen 64%
   Other gases 1%

Draw a 'pie' diagram similar to the one in Fig. 3.3 for
the air dissolved in water.
   In one sentence, summarize the difference between
the composition of ordinary air and that of the air
dissolved in water.

5 In *Foundation Skills – Chemistry* Volume 1 Unit 24 the topic of acid rain was discussed. Here is another article on the subject. Read the article and answer the questions which follow.

The term 'acid rain' is not a new one. It was first used in 1872. The emission of sulphur dioxide, mainly from burning fossil fuels, and nitrogen dioxide, mainly from vehicle exhausts, greatly contribute to acid levels in the atmosphere. Both sulphur dioxide and nitrogen dioxide are readily soluble in water, reacting with water to form sulphurous acid and nitrous acid respectively.

Rain is naturally acid with a pH of about 5 due to dissolved carbon dioxide forming carbonic acid. The dissolved sulphur dioxide and nitrogen dioxide reduce the pH of the rain and cause particular problems. See Table 3.1 and Fig. 3.4.

Great efforts are now being made to reduce sulphur dioxide emissions from power stations. Desulphurization of flue gases from a power station can remove 95% of the sulphur dioxide produced. This can be achieved by washing the flue gases with a suitable alkali solution.

(a) What are 'fossil fuels'?

(b) Write word equations for the reactions of sulphur dioxide, nitrogen dioxide and carbon dioxide with water.

(c) Sulphur dioxide and nitrogen dioxide dissolve in water to form acid solutions. These are further oxidized by oxygen in the air. What are the products of this oxidation?

(d) What is the approximate pH of:

    (i) pure water;

    (ii) dilute hydrochloric acid;

    (iii) rain over eastern Britain?

(e) A new power station is being built on the coast to produce electricity from coal imported from abroad. What are the advantages of building the power station on the coast?

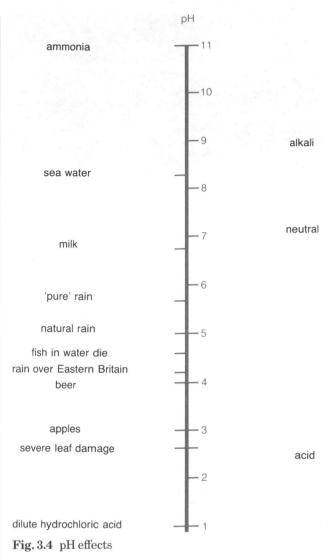

Fig. 3.4 pH effects

A possible solution to the problem of acid rain?

BREAD CURE FOR ACID RAIN

Mouldy bread may help to reduce acid rain in Europe. Scientists at North Staffordshire Polytechnic, Stoke-on-Trent, discovered a method of taking inorganic sulphur out of coal using Thiobacillus ferroxidous, a bacterium found in mouldy bread.

Summary

Gases are less soluble in water than solid solutes. The gases ammonia and hydrogen chloride are very soluble, however.

When a gas dissolves well in water it reacts with the water to form either an acid or an alkaline solution.

The solubility of a gas decreases with increasing temperature.

Unit 4

Water supply

Every day each one of us uses approximately 120 litres (26 gallons) of water. This water is taken from a clean river, reservoir or underground source. After being used the water must be treated before it can safely be returned to a river.
The supply of water in Great Britain and the treatment of waste water is in the hands of Water Authorities.

In this Unit we are going to consider where our water comes from, how it is treated and methods of 'cleaning up' water after use. This can be summarized in the water cycle in Fig. 4.1.

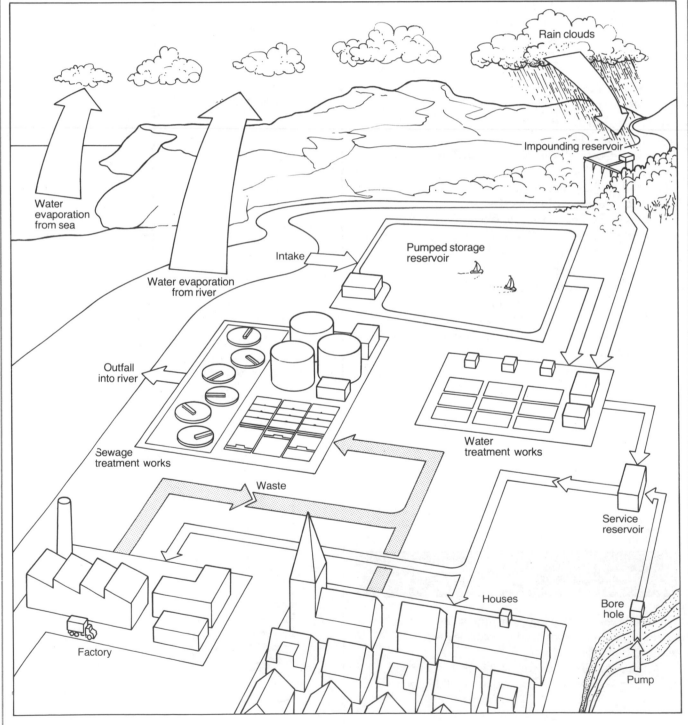

Fig. 4.1 The water cycle

4.1 Where does our water come from?

Water evaporates from seas, rivers and lakes and rises into the atmosphere until the air temperature cools down enough for the evaporated water to form clouds. The clouds travel on air currents until natural cooling causes the water in the clouds to fall as rain.

Some of the water falling on the ground flows into streams and rivers, lakes or man-made reservoirs. Water may be taken from clean rivers, lakes or reservoirs.

Water which does not run off into streams etc soaks into the ground. It passes through the rocks until it reaches an impermeable or 'water sealing' layer of rocks such as clay. It cannot pass through this and can only travel horizontally through the ground. The natural level of water in the ground is called the 'water table'. This may be near the surface or many feet below it.

Sometimes water-containing rocks like sandstone reach the surface of the ground and water may flow out of the ground as a **spring**. Usually, however, holes have to be bored into the ground to get the water. If the hole is shallow and of large diameter, it is termed a **well**. Deeper, narrower holes are drilled by machine and are called **boreholes**.

4.2 Treatment of tap water

Water that is drawn from rivers, lakes and reservoirs or underground rocks is not pure and has to be treated before it can be used as tap water.

The most undesirable features of the water may be:

▶ **Colour** – due to dissolved organic matter e.g. from peaty land;
▶ **Suspended matter** – mineral and vegetable matter;
▶ **Cloudiness** – fine mineral matter e.g. clay;
▶ **Harmful germs** and bacteria;
▶ **Hardness** – see Unit 5;
▶ **Taste and odour** – due to sewage, decayed vegetation or lack of oxygen in the water.

Various methods can be used in purification depending upon the impurities. These methods include:

1 Storage of water in lakes or reservoirs. During the storage suspended matter sinks to the bottom and harmful bacteria die out. The colour is bleached out by sunlight and contamination is reduced by contact with oxygen in the air.

2 Air is bubbled through water. This will remove odours and oxidize mineral salts making their removal easier.

3 Precipitation. Addition of chemicals such as alum or iron(II) sulphate will precipitate mineral salts.

4 Filtration. Precipitates can be removed from water by filtration. Rather than filter through paper as we do in the laboratory, the filtering is done through a sand filter (Fig. 4.2).

5 Disinfection. The last stage is to kill all harmful bacteria by bubbling the poisonous gas chlorine through the water. This process may be called chlorination.

At the end of this process the water is in a form which is safe and suitable for household use. It should be clear, colourless and odourless with no unpleasant taste. It should contain no harmful bacteria or mineral salts. It is not pure water, however, but still contains dissolved solids and dissolved gases.

Fig. 4.2 Filtering through sand

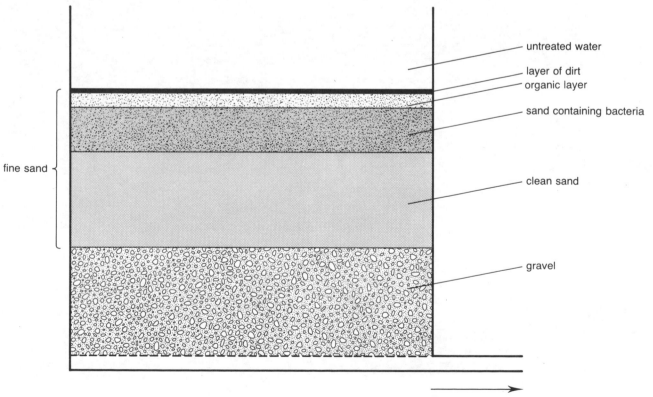

untreated water
layer of dirt
organic layer
sand containing bacteria
fine sand
clean sand
gravel
filtered water

Fig. 4.3 Well-dressing

4.3 Treatment of sewage

The waste water from our homes and from drains in the roads has to be purified in a sewage works before it can safely be returned to a river.

The purification of waste water usually involves three stages:

1 Removal of solids

The sewage is passed through metal screens to remove rags, pieces of wood etc which might later block pipes.

The crude sewage is then passed through large channels where sand and coarse dirt settle out. These solids are called sludge.

2 Removing organic waste

Organic waste is removed by bacteria. The waste water slowly trickles through a bed of gravel. The bacteria live on the gravel and, with the help of oxygen from the air, the bacteria feed on the organic matter.

3 Removing nitrates and phosphates

Nitrates and phosphates may still be present and they can be harmful in rivers. They may be removed before the water is pumped into a river.

At this stage the water is pure enough to be pumped back into a river and re-used for water supplies.

Fig. 4.4 Sewage works

Activities

1 Everyone uses an average of 120 litres of water each day. This comprises:

WC flushing and waste disposal	39 litres
washing and bathing	37 litres
laundering	20 litres
dishwashing and cleaning	12 litres
gardening	4 litres
drinking and cooking	6 litres
car washing	2 litres

Draw a pie diagram to show how we use our water. Remember each litre of water will be represented by an angle of 3°.

2 In this country we are very fortunate to have a safe water supply. Much of the disease in underdeveloped countries can be traced back to a poor water supply and lack of sewage treatment. Keep any newspaper cuttings you can find about water supplies and disease caused by lack of good water systems.

3 In Great Britain the years 1976 and 1984 were particularly noted for extremely dry drought periods. Read the following article about drought and answer the questions which follow.

Drought

1976 is a year which will go down in history because it was so dry – the driest for at least 250 years. Not only was it so dry, but there were consistently high temperatures which parched the countryside and broke records in many places.

Large amounts of water are used by industry. If these supplies had been cut off for long periods to conserve supplies it could have caused many problems. A problem which water authorities have in times of water shortage is deciding which firms should be exempted from cuts if rationing is introduced. Obvious examples would be food and manufacturing industries and hospitals.

Cuts to industry were avoided in 1976 by reducing water pressures in mains, cutting supplies to the public for certain periods and through voluntary savings made by industry.

The public played their part by cutting down domestic consumption and re-cycling their water. The Water Authority appealed for a 40% reduction but the best achieved was just over half that amount. Heavy rain over big cities was followed by a rise in consumption.

The lack of rain had drastic effects on the farm. The yield of wheat, barley and oats was down. Vegetables did not get the water that they need to swell.

Many farmers realized the value of boreholes. Many more farmers asked for permission to sink boreholes.

The worst damage to wildlife was not caused by the drought but by the side effect of it – **fire**. The majority of fires broke out on heathland and plants and animals living and growing in that type of habitat were the ones most affected.

The very dry summer of 1976 was followed by the worst floods for 20 years in the winter of 1976 – 77.

(a) Give three ways in which savings were made to prevent cuts in supplies to industry.

(b) What advice would you give to householders about how to save water during a drought?

(c) Why does heavy rain over Birmingham or Coventry not greatly alter the amount of tap water available?

(d) What would happen to the water table during a drought? What effect could this have on wells and boreholes?

Summary

Our water supply comes from clean rivers, lakes or reservoirs. The water is treated and chlorinated before being supplied to homes and industry.

The waste water is 'cleaned up' in a sewage works and then pumped back into the river.

Did you know

1 It takes

85 litres (18.7 gallons) of water for a bath;

9 – 13 litres (2 – 3 gallons) to wash your hands under a running tap;

9 litres (2 gallons) to flush the toilet cistern;

7 litres (1½ gallons) to make a pint of beer;

45 000 litres (10 000 gallons) to make a tonne of steel;

55 litres (12 gallons) to make a pound of instant coffee;

26 000 litres (5 800 gallons) to make one tonne of newspaper.

2 The biggest user of water is the power stations. Water is used in the making of electricity.

3 The human body is two-thirds water. If you lose 10% of your body water you will not be able to walk. If you lose 20% you will die.

4 Lettuces and cucumbers are 95% water.

5 Some places in Africa and India have an average of 10 160 cm (400 inches) of rain a year, but in parts of Chile there hasn't been a drop of rain for four centuries.

6 Rainfall in Britain varies in different parts of the country. Essex is the driest with an average of 508 mm (20 inches) a year, but in the mountains of Wales and the Lake District it is 4 064 mm (160 inches).

Unit 5

Hard and soft water

The water that comes from the tap varies greatly in different areas. Much depends upon the area from which the water is taken. The distinction between soft and hard water can be seen when washing with soap. Soft water lathers easily with soap without forming any precipitate or scum. Hard water wastes soap as the soap reacts with the impurities in the water to form scum. Hard water does not lather easily.

5.1 What causes hardness in water?

An experiment can be carried out to find the causes of hardness in water. Equal volumes of solutions of different chemicals are measured into separate test tubes. An equal volume of soap solution is added to each test tube. Each test tube is shaken. The height of lather in each test tube is measured. The results of an experiment are shown in Table 5.1.

Solution of	Height of lather (mm)	Is a scum or precipitate formed?
Sodium sulphate	25	No
Magnesium sulphate	2	Yes
Potassium chloride	30	No
Calcium chloride	1	Yes
Sodium nitrate	28	No
Magnesium nitrate	2	Yes
Calcium nitrate	2	Yes

Table 5.1 Results of an experiment to find causes of water hardness

Fig. 5.1 (a) Stalactites and stalagmites

From the results in Table 5.1 it can be concluded that little lather is formed and a scum is produced if either calcium or magnesium is present in the solution. Hardness in water is caused by dissolved calcium or magnesium compounds.

5.2 How does hardness get into water?

Rain water contains some dissolved carbon dioxide which forms carbonic acid and makes natural rain slightly acidic (pH 5). There are no calcium or magnesium compounds present in rain water and rain water is therefore completely soft.

When rain water trickles through the ground it will dissolve any soluble rocks. The most important rocks which dissolve are gypsum (calcium sulphate) and limestone or chalk (calcium carbonate). Calcium sulphate is only very slightly soluble. Calcium carbonate is insoluble in pure water but is soluble in rain water because of the presence of carbonic acid. When calcium carbonate dissolves in rainwater the unstable calcium hydrogencarbonate is formed.

In some limestone areas the dissolving away of rock can lead to the formation of large underground caverns. In these caverns hard water containing calcium hydrogencarbonate dripping from the ceiling can form either stalactites or stalagmites (see Fig. 5.1).

5.3 Hard water in England and Wales

Fig. 5.2 shows a geological map of England and Wales. In general, water is hard in the south and east because of calcium-containing rocks such as chalk, limestone and gypsum. In the north and west of England and Wales, the water is softer because rocks containing calcium are rarer.

5.4 Types of hardness

There are two basic types of hardness called permanent and temporary hardness. Temporary hardness is caused by dissolved calcium hydrogencarbonate. On boiling water containing temporary hardness, the calcium hydrogencarbonate decomposes and the hardness is removed. The decomposition of calcium hydrogencarbonate forms 'fur' or 'scale' in kettles or pipes.

Permanent hardness is caused by dissolved calcium sulphate and magnesium sulphate. These compounds are not changed when water containing permanent hardness is boiled. Permanent hardness is not removed by boiling.

5.5 Methods of removing hardness

The removal of calcium and magnesium compounds from hard water is called softening. The resulting water will then lather well with a minimum of soap.

Softening water can be done by distillation (see *Foundation Skills – Chemistry* Volume 1 Unit 10). This is an expensive process, however, and is not widely used unless a very cheap source of energy is available. The resulting water is not only soft, it is pure!

Water containing temporary hardness can be softened by boiling.

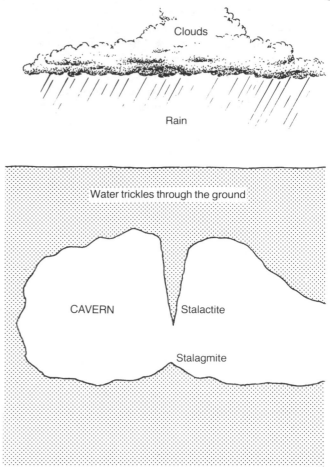

Fig. 5.1 (b) Formation of stalactites and stalagmites

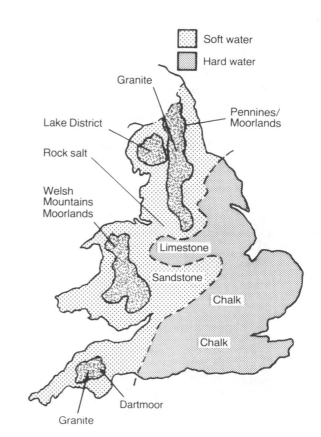

Fig. 5.2 Hard and soft water in England and Wales

Adding certain chemicals called softening agents will remove hardness from water. Suitable chemicals include sodium carbonate crystals (called washing soda) and 'Calgon' (sodium metaphosphate). These chemicals react with the calcium and magnesium compounds dissolved in hard water to form insoluble precipitates. The water is softened because calcium and magnesium are removed from the water.

The most important way of softening hard water is with an ion exchange column in a water softener (see Fig. 5.3). The ion exchange column contains a special resin which contains an excess of sodium compounds. When hard water runs through the column the sodium replaces the calcium and magnesium compounds in the water. The resulting water now contains no calcium and magnesium compounds and is soft. From time to time salt is added to the water softener to replenish the sodium compounds. Water softeners are important in industry and at home in hard water areas. Domestic dishwashers may contain water softeners.

5.6 Advantages and disadvantages of hard water

Most of the disadvantages are on economic grounds. Hard water wastes soap and forms scum. The ring formed round the bath is not caused by dirt on you but by reaction between soap and hardness in water. Scale inside pipes, radiators and boilers make central heating systems less efficient. Hard water can also ruin special finishes on certain fabrics.

Hard water has a much better taste than soft water. It also supplies most of the calcium necessary for the growth of teeth and bones. Hard water is also better for making beer. In fact, the brewing industry at Burton-on-Trent was established because of hard water coming from deposits of calcium sulphate underground.

Much of the water going to houses goes through lead pipes at some stage. Soft water dissolves more lead from the inside of the pipes and this can cause health problems in soft water areas.

Fig. 5.4 A water softener

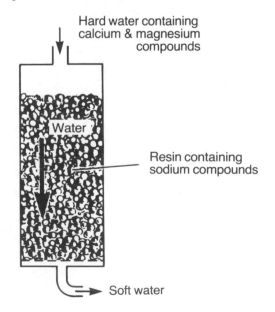

Fig. 5.3 Ion exchange column

Hard water containing calcium & magnesium compounds

Water

Resin containing sodium compounds

Soft water

Fig. 5.5 (a) 'Fur' in a kettle
(b) 'Fur' in a water pipe

Activities

*1 Making bath salts

Bath salts are added to the water to soften it. They can be made from sodium carbonate crystals or sodium sesquicarbonate. Sodium sesquicarbonate is a mixture of sodium carbonate and sodium hydrogencarbonate. It is less alkaline.

Mix some sodium sesquicarbonate crystals with a couple of drops of food colouring and perfume. You have now made some bath salts.

*2 Making temporary hard water

Add two teaspoonfuls of hydrated lime (calcium hydroxide – available from a garden shop) to a small bottle. Add water until the bottle is half full and stopper the bottle. You get the best results if you use water which has been boiled in a kettle and then allowed to cool. Shake the bottle and leave to stand until there is a clear solution above the solid. Carefully decant off the clear solution into a test tube until about 3 cm depth of solution is in the test tube.

Now blow through the solution with a drinking straw. The solution will first go white and cloudy. If you continue blowing the solution will go clear again. This solution contains calcium hydrogencarbonate and contains temporary hardness.

*3 Testing the 'fur' in a kettle

Carefully scrape out some of the fur from a kettle into a test tube. Add a little vinegar and warm the solution. Observe what happens in the test tube.

4 An experiment was carried out to compare the hardness of four water samples labelled A, B, C and D.

25 cm^3 of water sample A was transferred to a conical flask. Soap solution was then added to the flask in small volumes until a lasting lather was formed.

The experiment was repeated with water samples B, C and D.

The results obtained are shown in Table 5.2.

Water sample	Volume of soap solution required cm^3
A	5.0
B	1.0
C	12.0
D	9.0

Table 5.2 Results of experiments on samples A to D

(a) Name a piece of apparatus suitable for
  (i) measuring out a 25 cm^3 sample of water;
  (ii) adding small accurately measured volumes of soap solution.
(b) Arrange the four solutions in order of hardness with the softest solution first.

Another experiment was carried out using water samples A, B, C and D. Each water sample was boiled before use and the experiment carried out as before. The results obtained are shown in Table 5.3.

Water sample	Volume of soap solution required cm^3
A	5.0
B	1.0
C	8.0
D	1.0

Table 5.3 Results of experiments on boiled samples A to D

(c) Which of the four water samples was distilled water?
(d) What can you conclude about the type or types of hardness present in the other three water samples?
(e) Washing soda was added to water sample B before carrying out the addition of soap solution. What volume of soap solution would be required now to give a lasting lather?

5 Jill was given two water samples. One sample was distilled water but the other contained some temporary hardness.

Describe carefully how she could find out which sample is which. You may be able to think of more than one way.

6 Soap flakes can be used in experiments to test for hardness in water.

5 cm^3 of distilled water was added to a test tube and a single soap flake added. After shaking a lather was formed in the test tube.

5 cm^3 samples of water containing
  (i) only permanent hardness;
  (ii) only temporary hardness;
  (iii) both permanent and temporary hardness
were put into separate test tubes. Soap flakes were added to each test tube until a lasting lather was produced. The test tube containing water with only temporary hardness required 9 soap flakes. The one containing water with permanent hardness only required 8 soap flakes and the one containing water with both types of hardness required 6 soap flakes.

The experiment was repeated after water samples had been boiled and after washing soda crystals had been added.

(a) Complete Table 5.4 using the information in the question.
(b) Drops of washing-up liquid were used in place of soap flakes. The results are shown in the right-hand column of Table 5.4.

Activities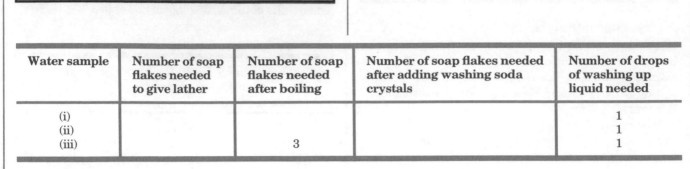

Water sample	Number of soap flakes needed to give lather	Number of soap flakes needed after boiling	Number of soap flakes needed after adding washing soda crystals	Number of drops of washing up liquid needed
(i)				1
(ii)				1
(iii)		3		1

Table 5.4 Results of an experiment testing water hardness

What can be concluded from these results in the right-hand column of Table 5.4?

7 An experiment was carried out using four aqueous solutions A, B, C and D.

  A = iron(II) sulphate solution
  B = sodium sulphate solution
  C = magnesium sulphate solution
  D = ammonium sulphate solution

  Equal volumes of A, B, C and D were measured into separate test tubes. A few drops of soap solution were added to each test tube and the test tubes shaken.

(a) Measure the height in mm of the lather in each test tube in Fig. 5.6. Record these results in Table 5.5.

Test tube containing solution	Height of lather mm
A	
B	
C	
D	

Table 5.5 Fill in the heights from Fig. 5.6

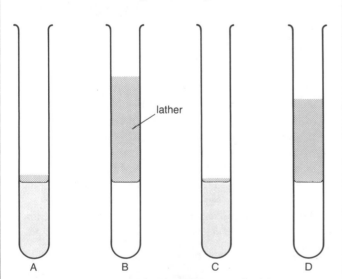

Fig. 5.6 Each tube was shaken with soap solution

(b) Hardness in water is caused by dissolved calcium and magnesium compounds. From these results name one other substance which causes hardness in water.

8 The following equations represent reactions involving water.

  A $Ca(HCO_3)_2(aq) \rightarrow CaCO_3(s) + H_2O(l) + CO_2(g)$
  B $CaCO_3(s) + H_2O(l) + CO_2(g) \rightarrow Ca(HCO_3)_2(aq)$
  C $CO_2(g) + H_2O(l) \rightarrow H_2CO_3(aq)$
  D $CaSO_4(aq) + Na_2CO_3(aq) \rightarrow CaCO_3(s)$
  $+ Na_2SO_4(aq)$

Which of these equations represents:
(a) the dissolving of carbon dioxide in rain;
(b) the dissolving of limestone in rain water;
(c) the decomposition of temporary hardness in water;
(d) the softening of permanent hardness in water?

9 After you have had a bath your mother complains about a 'ring' round the inside of the bath. This is caused, she says, because 'you don't have a bath often enough and you are dirty!'.

How could you show her simply that the 'ring' round the bath is really due to hardness of water?

Would this ring still form if you did not use soap but used a bubble bath containing a soapless detergent?

Summary

Pure water or distilled water lathers well with soap without forming any precipitate or scum. The presence of dissolved compounds in water, calcium and magnesium in particular, makes the water hard. This means that it does not lather well with soap but forms a scum or precipitate.

  There are two types of hardness:
Temporary hardness caused by calcium hydrogencarbonate dissolved in water. On boiling the calcium hydrogencarbonate decomposes and the hardness is removed. The resulting calcium carbonate forms a fur or scale.
Permanent hardness caused by dissolved calcium sulphate and magnesium sulphate. This is not removed by boiling.

  Water can be softened (i.e. have its hardness removed) by distillation, adding softening agents such as washing soda and by using a water softener.

  In many industries hard water increases costs either by wasting soap, forming scale which makes equipment less efficient or spoiling materials.

Unit 6

Detergents

The word 'detergent' means 'something which cleans'. A detergent can be used with water to make things clean. Detergents can be in the form of tablets, powders, flakes or liquids.
Detergents can be divided into two groups – **soaps** and **soapless detergents**.

6.1 Soaps

Soap was the first detergent to be made. There are references to soap in the Old Testament. It was made by mixing vegetable oils with an alkali containing potassium obtained from certain plants which grew in salt marshes.

Soap is still made by a similar process called saponification. Animal and/or vegetable fats or oils (called triglycerides) are boiled with a strong alkali such as sodium hydroxide or potassium hydroxide. The fats or oils are broken down by the alkali. The animal fats used include tallow and whale or fish oil. Palm, coconut, soya bean, groundnut and olive oils are common vegetable oils used for soap making.

Animal or
vegetable fat + alkali → soap + glycerol
or oil

Glycerol, more correctly called propane-1,2,3-triol, is a useful by-produce of soap making. The soap is separated from the products of saponification by adding salt (sodium chloride). The soap, which does not dissolve in salt solution, separates out as a solid precipitate.

6.2 Soapless detergents

Soapless detergents are made from chemicals called hydrocarbons produced during fractional distillation of crude oil or petroleum (see Unit 22). These chemicals are reacted with concentrated sulphuric acid in a process called sulphonation. The product is a soapless detergent.

6.3 Similarities and differences between soaps and soapless detergents

Soaps and soapless detergents are made up from tiny particles called molecules. In both cases the molecules can be considered to be made up of two parts:
1 A long hydrocarbon 'tail' which is hydrophobic, i.e. it does not like to mix with water;
2 A 'head' which is hydrophilic, i.e. it likes to mix with water.

A detergent molecule is shown in Fig. 6.1. The cleaning action of a soap or soapless detergent depends upon the peculiar shape and properties of these little 'tadpole' molecules.

Soapless detergents have one big advantage. They lather well without forming scum in all types of water. Soaps, however, lather well in soft water (see Unit 5) but do not lather well in hard water.

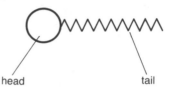

head   tail

Fig. 6.1 A detergent molecule

6.4 Cleaning action of detergents

Fig. 6.2 summarizes the cleaning action of detergents.

Water is not a good wetting agent. If a detergent is added to water it will more thoroughly wet the cloth (see Activities).

The tails of the detergent molecules stick into grease. Because the heads of the detergent molecules are attracted to the water molecules, the grease is lifted from the material.

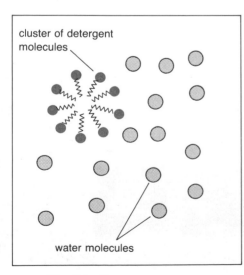

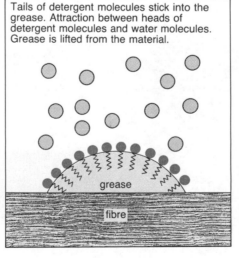

Tails of detergent molecules stick into the grease. Attraction between heads of detergent molecules and water molecules. Grease is lifted from the material.

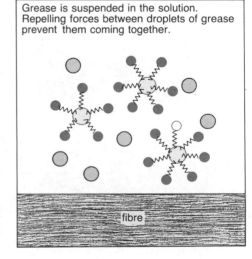

Grease is suspended in the solution. Repelling forces between droplets of grease prevent them coming together.

Fig. 6.2 Cleaning action of detergents

Activities

*1 Detergents lower the surface tension of water and improve the wetting of material.

You can get a needle to float on water if you are very careful. Fill a dish half full of clean water and float a small piece of paper about 5 cm square on the surface of the water. Carefully place a needle on the paper and push the paper down so that it sinks. If you are lucky the needle will remain floating on the surface of the water. This is due to a 'skin' over the water called surface tension.

Now very carefully add a couple of drops of washing-up liquid to the water. What do you observe?

Take a piece of cloth such as cotton. Put a couple of drops of water onto the cloth. Now add a couple of drops of water containing washing-up liquid to the cloth. What observations can you make each time?

*2 **Compare different brands of washing powder**

A great deal of money is spent each year advertising different brands of washing powder. Given ordinary household apparatus, devise an experiment to compare different washing powders to find out which one 'washes whitest'.

3 The photograph (Fig. 6.3) shows one of the problems of early detergents. Modern detergents are 'bio-degradable'. Describe the problems shown in the photograph and explain why this does not happen today.

Fig. 6.3 Early detergents foaming in a river

4 Fig. 6.4 is a pie diagram showing the composition of a brand of washing powder.

(a) Which substance is present in the largest amount in the washing powder?

(b) Is this washing powder likely to produce scum in a hard water area?

(c) If a sample of this washing powder is left exposed to air it gains in mass. Which of the substances present will absorb water readily?

5 Some modern washing powders sometimes contain enzymes. What is the purpose of these added enzymes? Under what conditions do the enzyme washing powders work best?

6 The following passage concerns the history of detergents. Read the passage and answer the questions which follow.

Until the eighteenth century soap making was only a small industry. Most people made their own, rather impure soap using animal fat and ashes.

Several factors caused a rapid expansion of soap making in the late eighteenth and early nineteenth centuries. In 1787 it was shown that soda could be made from salt. This gave the soap maker access to large amounts of cheap alkali. A few years later the French chemist Chevreul showed that soap making was not just a matter of mixing but depended upon definite chemical reactions.

During the nineteenth century increased wages and living standards enabled ordinary people to buy soap for the first time. Tax on soap was abolished by Gladstone in 1853. Improved transport opened up new sources of fats and oils from Africa and Asia. The consumption of soap in Great Britain rose from 20 000 tonnes in 1820 to 90 000 tonnes in 1853 and 300 000 tonnes by 1900.

Fig. 6.5 A Tudor tablet of soap with a fish emblem

Between 1900 and 1910 there was a world shortage of animal fats. Soap makers looked for alternative raw materials. Tropical oils such as palm oil had not been used as they were considered too runny. A method of 'hardening' or hydrogenating oils was discovered in Germany and introduced in Great Britain in 1911. This made tropical oils suitable.

In 1831 a French chemist had shown that a synthetic soapless detergent could be made by treating castor oil with sulphuric acid. This did not find immediate success.

Soapless detergents did not become popular until the 1950s when the high price of natural fats and oils coupled with increased demand made their development essential.

(a) What is the meaning of the word 'synthetic'?

(b) Give two reasons why soap making was introduced into North Cheshire along the River Mersey.

(c) Give the reasons why the price of soap fell during the nineteenth century.

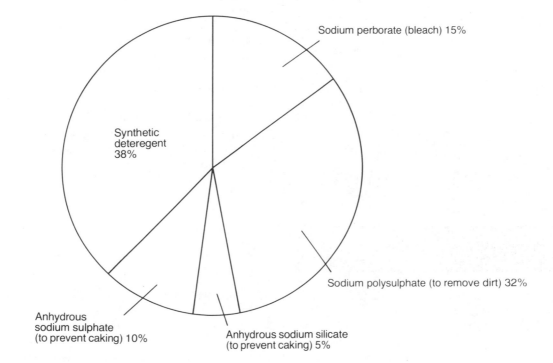

Fig. 6.4 Composition of a washing powder

Sodium perborate (bleach) 15%

Synthetic deteregent 38%

Sodium polysulphate (to remove dirt) 32%

Anhydrous sodium sulphate (to prevent caking) 10%

Anhydrous sodium silicate (to prevent caking) 5%

Activities continued

7 Read the following article about the effects of washing.

Over-washing is unhealthy

HUNDREDS of years ago, people knew, instinctively, that washing was unhealthy!

Of course we've progressed since then — but has the pendulum swung too far in the opposite direction? Many scientists and doctors, in fact, are now convinced that it is possible to wash too much.

In America, it's not unknown for the wealthier classes to shower six times a day. Apparently, these people seem to suffer more skin complaints than any others.

One doctor, researching the possibility that in some cases washing can do you more damage than good, had no lack of volunteers!

Insulting

According to the doctor washing really makes the skin susceptible to contamination by bacteria, and that it can therefore be harmful.

Soap has been around for nearly two thousand years. But for all that the doctor says: "In ordinary life the cleansing of the skin with soap, apart from special hazards, is not of great medical importance."

Soap has some benefits, he admits, but he reckons that the disadvantages may well outweigh them. The advantages of using soap are that it removes grease and dirt, so that skin looks cleaner. It does away with body odour caused by sweat and grease. And it also helps to cut down the risk of infection, especially among people handling food.

Yet many scientists now feel that you may well be insulting your skin by using soap.

The whole problem arises because of the complicated structure of the skin . . . because of the way in which it is specially geared to look after itself.

Outside is the corneous layer, the thickness of which varies with the position of the body. On the palms of the hand and the soles of the feet it is up to two millimetres thick, but on the face it is somewhat less than 0.01 millimetres thick.

Under this outer surface is a section made up of layer upon layer of cells. However, the main bulk of the skin comes under these two sections. This is called the dermis, which is fibrous tissue consisting of blood vessels, nerves and glands, and it is often three millimetres thick. It is these two outer layers, and the qualities they have, which bring the accusation that soap and washing can be harmful.

These two outer layers are known collectively as the epidermis, and are much affected by alteration in their chemical make-up. They are specially geared by nature to act as a barrier against all possibly harmful things, from germs to dirt.

Part of this wonderful protection is provided by a kind of emulsion, and this is where soap becomes the villain. It not only takes the dirt off the skin, but also washes away this natural protective emulsion.

The surface of the skin is normally acid, and this helps in protecting the lower skin or dermis. Soap, unfortunately, breaks down this buffer system.

Research has shown it takes a full 1½ hours for the skin to return to normal acid level after washing. Germs falling on the skin during that time after washing can have a clear way in to the lower skin.

Soap thus destroys the skin's own mechanism for killing off germs. So, although soap cleans the skin of many germs, it also makes it more susceptible than usual for fresh contamination to occur.

It has been shown that people who have contact with soap for long periods, like housewives or factory workers, are in danger of things like chapping and dermatitis.

Discoveries

Manufacturing scientists are researching soapless cleansers. These synthetic detergents contain chemicals which will not destroy the body's own defence mechanism. They will undoubtedly be 'neutral' substances, not highly alkali nor acid.

But they're also taking stock of cleansing with ultrasonic waves — so high-pitched we can't hear them — and the soap-like products produced by herbs and various mud-like and Fuller's Earth compounds.

In the wake of these discoveries comes an electronic device to save the trouble of washing! It is claimed to emit high range energy waves that sweep the skin's surface and clean it by electronic means.

Users say their skin feels rejuvenated, as if it has been lifted and energized. Some reckon it's as if they'd had a refreshing sauna.

(a) What are the advantages of using soap?
(b) What is the disadvantage of using soap?
(c) What advantages do soapless synthetic detergents have over soaps?

Summary

Detergents are cleaning agents. There are two types of detergent – soaps and soapless detergents.

Soaps are made by boiling natural fats and oils with strong alkali. Soapless detergents are made by treating hydrocarbons with sulphuric acid.

Detergents are made up of 'tadpole' molecules. They clean by:

1 reducing the surface tension of the water and wetting the cloth;

2 separating dirt from the fibres of the cloth; and

3 keeping dirt suspended in the water.

Soapless detergents lather in hard or soft water without forming scum. Soap forms scum in hard water.

Unit 7

Water pollution

Over fifty million gallons of waste water are discharged from sewage works, factories and farms into rivers in Great Britain each day. Despite the growing volume of waste water, the condition of our rivers and estuaries has improved out of all recognition. This is due to the vigilance of chemists and improvements in experimental methods.

7.1 Dissolved oxygen in water

In Unit 3 you will find out that oxygen is only very slightly soluble in cold water. The solubility decreases as temperature rises.

Even slight river pollution will, through a variety of chemical reactions, use up this small amount of oxygen. Then all river life becomes impossible.

Fortunately a river can recover from slight pollution. Oxygen from the air will dissolve in polluted water.

Fig. 7.1 Fast-flowing rivers soon replace lost oxygen

7.2 Pollution by nitrogen compounds

A major source of pollution is nitrogen, often in the form of ammonium compounds. Bacteria in the water oxidize the ammonia to form nitrates using up the oxygen in the water. Because nitrates encourage the growth of plants, water with high nitrate levels can be recognized by the growth of green algae on the surface. This prevents light getting into the water. When this algae dies it decays, removing further oxygen.

Eventually the water will contain no life. This type of nitrogen pollution is caused by discharges of sewage and, more commonly these days, waste water from farms. If a farmer uses excess or unwise nitrogen fertilizers the excess nitrogen fertilizer finds itself in local streams and rivers. Water Authorities carefully monitor discharges of water from farms in an effort to reduce water pollution.

There are serious questions being asked at present about health risks associated with high nitrate levels in water.

HEALTH RISK FROM NITRATES IN WATER

By Our Health Services Correspondent

Rising levels of nitrates from fertilisers are posing a potential health risk to water supplies, the Royal Society said in a scientific report yesterday.

It said that nitrate concentrations in river water were now up to four times higher than 20 years ago and a close watch should be kept on any further increase.

Some rivers, particularly in the Midlands and South-East, already had a nitrate level which exceeded the World Health Organisation's recommended limit for drinking water.

7.3 Heavy metal pollution

Metals discharged into rivers in the forms of soluble compounds can cause many problems.

Metals such as lead, cadmium and iron are removed as far as is possible before water is discharged into a river.

7.4 Pollution in the River Thames

The situation in the River Thames is typical of other rivers in Great Britain. Because of careful work by the Thames Water Authority the quality of water in the river has improved greatly. Fig. 7.2 shows some of the 90 species of fish which can now be caught in the River Thames. Water can be withdrawn from the river for drinking purposes.

In the nineteenth century the river was particularly unhealthy because of the growth of population in London and increased industry. The year 1858 was called the 'Year of the Great Stink'. A great sewer building programme followed but apart from the smell, the river was unhealthy.

The most serious problem was cholera. Cholera came to Great Britain from India. Every year it killed thousands of people in London. John Snow showed that polluted water caused cholera in 1854. Later it was found that a virus in water caused the disease. The last outbreak of cholera in Great Britain was in 1937 when 43 people died in Croydon. Cholera still affects people in parts of the world where a clean water supply is not available.

Pope travels where water is a luxury

Residents of the Lima slum of San Juan De Dios never have to worry about drinking bad tap water because their homes have no taps. There is no electricity, either, in a grimy shanty town of more than 10,000 people.

Instead, the slum-dwellers get their water from an ancient lorry that delivers twice a week. For a price three times as high as water through the mains, the driver will pump 40 gallons into a rusting oil drum kept on the doorstep.

If someone wants a wash they dip a saucepan in the beaten-up oil drum, flicking away floating insects and trying to avoid scooping up the thin layer of scum. In these squalid tin-roofed shacks of San Juan De Dios, there are no lavatories, just holes in the mud at the back.

If the water is used for cooking or drinking it must first be strained and boiled or the family will soon catch typhoid. Many residents have had hepatitis, many suffer from worms that settle in their intestines to feed off their stomachs. Tuberculosis, once all but eradicated in Peru, is making an ominous comeback.

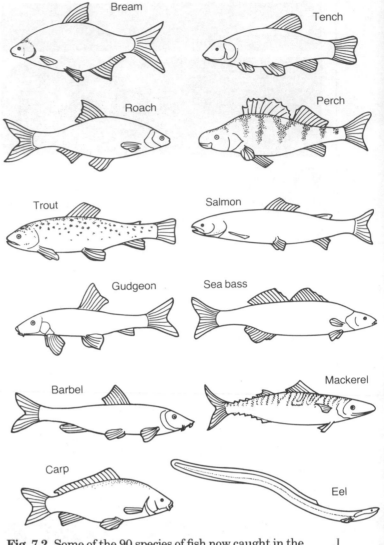

Fig. 7.2 Some of the 90 species of fish now caught in the Thames

Fig. 7.3 Father Thames introduces his offspring to the fair city of London

Activities

1 Fig. 7.4 shows a sketch map of a river. Water samples were taken at seven places along the river labelled A to G. These samples were analysed and the results are shown in Table 7.1.

Sample	A	B	C	D	E	F	G
Temperature (°C)	6	7	6	6	10	7	6
pH	7	9	6	6	6	6	8
Dissolved oxygen (parts per million)	14	9	12	9	9	12	11
Free ammonia (parts per million)	0	10	2	7	6	2	3
Nitrates (parts per million)	0	0	4	7	8	5	9

Table 7.1 Analysis of seven samples taken from a river

(a) Which sample A to G:
   (i) is most pure;
   (ii) is at the highest temperature;
   (iii) is exactly neutral;
   (iv) contains the most free ammonia?
(b) Explain the difference between the:
   (i) pH of A and B;
   (ii) dissolved oxygen levels of B and C;
   (iii) free ammonia levels of C and D;
   (iv) temperature of D and E;
   (v) dissolved oxygen levels of E and F;
   (vi) nitrate levels of F and G?

2 Table 7.2 shows some small water creatures which can exist in water containing different amounts of pollution.

A river was examined at four places (W, X, Y and Z) and the only creatures present in the water are shown in Table 7.3.

Arrange the four waters in order of pollution with the least polluted sample first.

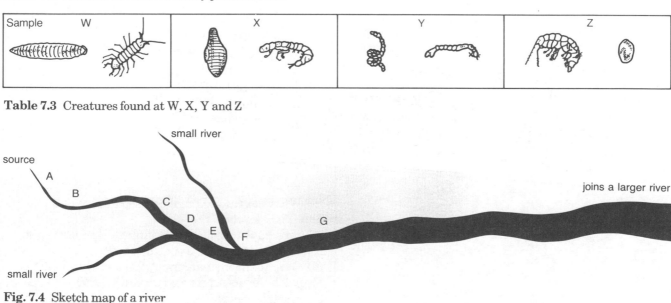

Amount of pollution	Animals found		
Very high			
High			
Low			
Very low			

Table 7.2 Animals found in variously polluted water

Sample W	X	Y	Z

Table 7.3 Creatures found at W, X, Y and Z

Fig. 7.4 Sketch map of a river

Activities continued

3 Read the following article about water pollution in the Lake District and answer the questions which follow.

ACIDITY LEVELS HELD DOWN IN LAKE DISTRICT

There is no evidence of a progressive long-term increase in acidity levels of Lake District waters that have been tested every week over the past 30 years, the assistant director of the Windermere-based Freshwater Biological Association said yesterday.

He was speaking after a visit the previous day by the House of Commons Select Committee on the Environment, which is looking into the effects of acid rain.

He said he told the committee that some of the lakes, Windermere, Esthwaite Water, and Blelham Tarn, showed a decrease in acidity, particularly since the 1960s.

He attributed this to an increase in nitrate and phosphate coming in from the agricultural run-off from fertilizers used on the fields, and increased inputs of nutrients into the lakes from the sewage treatment plants which, since the 1960s, have replaced the septic tanks that were once common in the area.

"So the lakes have had essentially more nutrients, more foodstuffs, and they become more productive and more algae have grown, and these lakes have less acidity."

The effect of the increased nutrients in the waters of these lakes had been to counteract some of the possible changes due to acidity, Dr Kinsman said.

While analysis of rainfall in the Lake District over the last 30 years had shown no progressive change in the acidity levels of the rain, it was still "extremely acid", he said.

Acidity is measured by what is called pH level. The lower the figure, the greater the acidity, and the higher the figure, the greater the alkalinity. Normal rain has a pH value of 5.6, said Edinburgh University's Forestry and Natural Resources Department.

Extremely acid

They said yesterday: "In the Lake District, our evidence from analysis of rainfall, spread over a 30-year period, shows that the acidity of rain does not show any progressive change, and has stayed at a value of 4.4pH over the last 30 years. It is extremely acid, between five and 10 times more acid than normal rainfall."

The increase in agricultural productivity (more head of livestock on the land, growing more grass to support that livestock, involving either spreading of animal sludge or particularly nitrogen-based fertilizers) all led to an increase in nitrate run-off through the land and into water sources, both ground water and rivers.

"This is a growing problem, and I think it is something the farming community needs to be made aware of," but it did reduce the acidity of the water.

"Our natural waters have very low nitrate concentrations. In the South of England this leaching through the soil has raised the dissolved nitrate levels to close to acceptable health levels.

"In the Lake District, our nitrate concentrations are naturally much lower. We have much purer waters, with normally much lower nitrogen in them, so they can take a much greater nitrate pollution to get to the sorts of levels down South, but the effect of increased nutrients has been to counteract some of the possible changes due to acidity."

(a) What has caused the increased nitrate and phosphate levels in the lakes?

(b) How have these increased nitrate and phosphate levels shown themselves in the lakes?

(c) Despite the increase in nitrate and phosphate levels, there has been no change in pH. Why has no change taken place?

4 Fig. 7.5 shows the concentration of some metals in mud in different estuaries around Great Britain. The levels are shown as a percentage (for iron) or in $\mu g/g$ (micrograms per gram – a microgram is a millionth of a gram).

Use Fig. 7.5 to answer the following questions.

(a) Which estuaries contain:

(i) most mercury in the mud;

(ii) most copper and lead in the mud;

(iii) most cadmium in the mud?

(b) Explain how these heavy metals might come to be in the samples of mud analysed.

Summary

Water pollution is a serious subject. Great improvements have been made to rivers, lakes and estuaries. Much of this has involved the control of water pumped from sewage works, farms and factories. These waters are called effluents.

The most serious problem we face is probably high nitrate levels caused by fertilizers being washed into rivers. The health problems caused by high nitrate levels are not understood.

Fig. 7.5 Concentrations of some metals in estuary mud

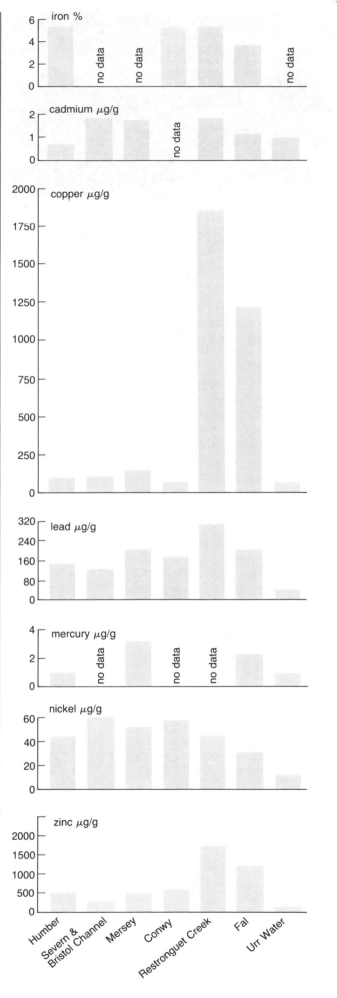

Unit 8

Crystals and water of crystallization

When a hot, saturated solution of copper(II) sulphate solution is left to stand and cool, blue crystals of copper sulphate crystals are formed (Fig. 8.1). If the solution is cooled quickly small crystals are formed. Larger crystals will be produced if the crystallization takes place slowly.

The shape of the copper(II) sulphate crystals is always the same. These crystals contain a fixed quantity of trapped water called water of crystallization. This water of crystallization is lost on heating.

Some crystals form without water of crystallization e.g. sodium chloride NaC1 and some with water of crystallization e.g. sodium carbonate crystals $Na_2CO_3.10H_2O$.

8.1 Showing that crystals contain water of crystallization

Fig. 8.2 shows apparatus suitable for showing that crystals contain water of crystallization. Some dry crystals are placed in the horizontal test tube. The test tube is heated and steam is produced. The steam is condensed by the cold water in the beaker and the

Fig. 8.1 Copper (II) sulphate crystal

colourless liquid collects in the test tube.

The solid remaining in the horizontal test tube has had its water of crystallization removed and is said to be anhydrous.

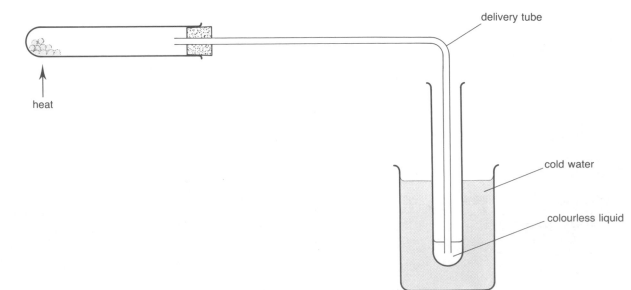

heat

delivery tube

cold water

colourless liquid

Fig. 8.2 Apparatus to show water of crystallization

Fig. 8.3 Crystals in nature

(a) Fluorite (calcium fluoride)

(b) Galena (lead (II) sulphate)

(c) Barytes (barium sulphate)

(d) Calcite (calcium carbonate)

(e) Sulphur

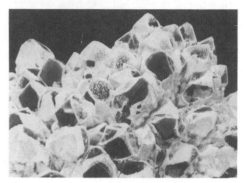

(f) Amethyst – a variety of quartz (silicon dioxide)

8.2 Crystals

Crystals are solids with regular shapes. They are formed when either a molten substance or a saturated solution cools. Many substances in nature exist as crystals (see photographs in Fig. 8.3).

A crystal is formed because all of the particles in the crystal line up to form a regular shape (see Fig. 8.4).

A crystal can be split cleanly with a razor blade in a direction parallel to one of its faces. The small pieces obtained are the same shape as the original crystal. This splitting is shown in Fig. 8.5 and is called cleaving a crystal. Information about the arrangement of particles in a crystal can be obtained by considering the directions in which cleavage is possible.

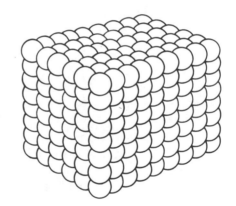

Fig. 8.4 Regular alignment of particles in a crystal

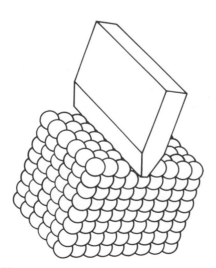

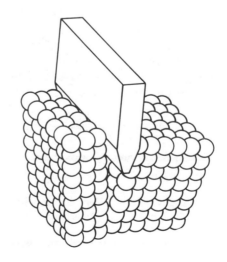

Fig. 8.5 Cleaving a crystal

48

Activities

1 There is only a limited number of possible crystal shapes. Fig. 8.6 shows how you can make models of the different crystal shapes from cardboard.

2 The following questions refer to the experiment shown in Fig. 8.2.

(a) The apparatus has to be supported. Where should the apparatus be clamped?

(b) During the experiment the colourless liquid in the test tube started to travel back up the delivery tube and into the horizontal test tube.

    (i) How could this be avoided?

    (ii) Why does it take place?

(c) How could you show that the colourless liquid collected is pure water?

3 Crystals of magnesium sulphate contain water of crystallization. Heating magnesium sulphate crystals produces anhydrous magnesium sulphate. The change can be represented by the equation:

$$MgSO_4.7H_2O \rightarrow MgSO_4 + 7H_2O$$

Some crystals of magnesium sulphate were heated in a crucible and the mass of the crucible and contents found at intervals during the heating.

The results were:

At the start of the experiment

    mass of crucible + crystals = 17.27 g

    mass of crucible   = 14.81 g

During the experiment

    1 mass of crucible + residue = 16.04 g

    2 mass of crucible + residue = 16.02 g

    3 mass of crucible + residue = 16.01 g

    4 mass of crucible + residue = 16.01 g

(a) Had all the water of crystallization been lost by the crystals when weighing **1** was carried out? Explain your answer.

(b) from the results, calculate the mass of:

    (i) crystals used;

    (ii) residue remaining at the end of the experiment;

    (iii) water of crystallization.

(c) Calculate the loss of mass if 246 g of magnesium sulphate crystals were heated.

4 A sample of hydrated iron(III) chloride is yellow/orange in colour. A sample was heated in the apparatus in Fig. 8.2. They changed to a red-brown colour and a colourless liquid was collected in the test tube as before.

The liquid was tested and the results obtained were as follows in Table 8.1:

Evaporation to dryness	No residue formed
pH	1
Electrical conductivity	Very good conductor
Add to cobalt(II) chloride paper	Turns from blue to pink

Table 8.1 Results of tests on the colourless liquid

(a) Which of the results obtained would **not** be expected if the colourless liquid was pure water?

(b) Which of the following conclusions is most likely to be correct on the basis of the information given?

A The colourless liquid collected contains iron(II) chloride.

B Reaction of iron(II) chloride produces an aqueous solution of an acid.

C Iron(III) chloride crystals are unchanged when heated.

D An alkaline solution is collected.

Summary

Crystals are solids with regular shapes. They may contain water of crystallization within the crystal. This is usually lost on heating. The solid remaining when water of crystallization is lost is usually powdery and is said to be anhydrous.

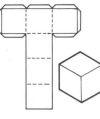
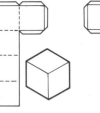

cubic   tetragonal

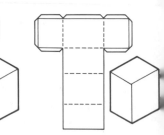

orthorhombic

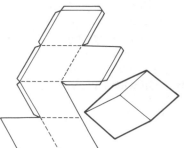

trigonal

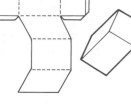

monoclinic

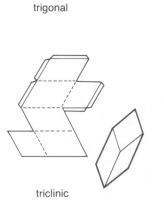

triclinic

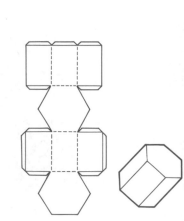

hexagonal

Fig. 8.6 Making models of crystal shapes – thick card is best

Unit 9

The effect of the atmosphere on chemicals

It is important not to keep chemicals in store for long periods. Schools are recommended to buy the quantities of each chemical to last only one year. The major reason for the spoilage of chemicals is the reaction between the chemical and a gas in the air. The three gases which have the greatest effect in spoiling chemicals are **oxygen**, **carbon dioxide** and **water vapour**.

Most other gases in the air are unreactive and have little effect.

The life of most chemicals is prolonged by keeping them in air-tight glass or plastic bottles. Often there is a plastic seal which fits under the lid.

9.1 Chemicals spoilt by oxygen

Many chemicals react with oxygen. This process is called oxidation. The process usually produces an increase in mass.

As an example of oxidation: lumps of calcium metal are a dull silver colour when new. They are quickly coated with a white powder. This is calcium oxide and eventually all of the calcium is converted into calcium oxide. Calcium oxide may in turn react with carbon dioxide and water vapour.
Green iron(II) compounds are oxidized to brown iron(III) compounds on exposure to the atmosphere.

9.2 Chemicals spoilt by carbon dioxide

Alkalis, in particular, absorb carbon dioxide from the atmosphere, e.g. calcium hydroxide absorbs carbon dioxide from the atmosphere to form calcium carbonate.

9.3 Chemicals spoilt by water vapour

Many chemicals absorb water vapour from the atmosphere. The amount of water which is absorbed can vary greatly from one compound to another. Some chemicals can also lose water vapour to the atmosphere.

9.4 Hygroscopic and deliquescent compounds

Hygroscopic and deliquescent compounds both absorb water vapour from the atmosphere over a period of days. Hygroscopic compounds e.g. copper(II) oxide only absorb very small amounts of water vapour. They are usually very little changed in appearance and the mass of the compound only increases by a very small amount.

Deliquescent compounds absorb large amounts of water and usually change drastically in appearance. An example is lithium chloride which is a white crystalline solid resembling salt. If some crystals of lithium chloride are left on a watch glass they absorb a large amount of water vapour. A pool of lithium chloride solution remains after a few days. Lithium chloride absorbs a large amount of water, sufficient to dissolve the crystals. There is a big increase in mass.

9.5 A desiccator

A desiccator (Fig. 9.1) is a piece of apparatus which is used to keep chemicals dry. At the bottom of the desiccator is a chemical which absorbs any water vapour in the air inside the desiccator. Anhydrous calcium chloride or silica gel are suitable chemicals for this purpose. The ground glass seal between the two halves of the desiccator prevents air from entering.

A desiccator may also be used to dry damp chemicals. The moisture in the chemical is eventually absorbed by the drying agent.

A desiccator should never be picked up by holding the glass knob on the lid.

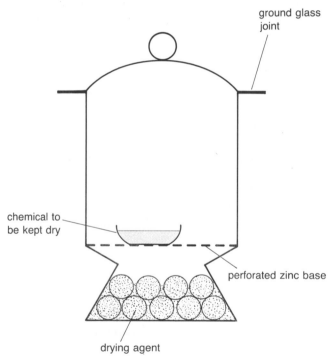

Fig. 9.1 A desiccator

9.6 Efflorescent compounds

(The word efflorescence should not be confused with the word effervescence).

Many chemicals contain water of crystallization e.g. washing soda $Na_2CO_3.10H_2O$. On standing in an open container, the colourless crystals lose water vapour and become a white powder. There is a decrease in mass. The formula of the white powder which remains is $Na_2CO_3.H_2O$.

Activities

Substance	Mass of sample fresh from a new bottle	Mass of the same sample after one week
A	12.95 g	13.07 g
B	11.85 g	30.13 g
C	12.34 g	12.34 g
D	13.45 g	9.85 g

Table 9.1 Changes in mass of substances exposed to the atmosphere

1 Which one of the four substances A – D in Table 9.1 is:

(a) unchanged on exposure to the atmosphere;
(b) deliquescent;
(c) efflorescent;
(d) hygroscopic?

2 Often the holes in the top of a salt cellar from a damp pantry become clogged. This can be prevented by mixing the table salt with a few grains of uncooked rice.

(a) Why does the salt cellar clog?
(b) Why does the rice not come out with the salt?
(c) What is the reason for putting rice grains in the salt cellar?
(d) Describe a simple experiment to show that rice grains act in this way.

3 A friend suggests that the change which occurs when a dry biscuit is left exposed to the atmosphere is caused by the biscuit losing certain chemicals to the atmosphere.

(a) How does the texture of a biscuit change on standing unwrapped for a few days?
(b) Explain clearly how you would attempt to disprove your friend's suggestion.
(c) What do you think causes this change in texture?

4 Silicon tetrachloride is a liquid which reacts with water vapour to produce large volumes of hydrogen chloride gas. Bottles of silicon tetrachloride have been known to explode while being stored especially if the bottle has a screw top.

(a) Explain why these bottles of silicon tetrachloride might explode.
(b) Suggest a safe way of storing a small volume of silicon tetrachloride.

5 A bag of crisps contains a dry, unreactive gas rather than air.

(a) Why is the bag not filled with ordinary air?
(b) Give one advantage to (i) the purchaser and (ii) the manufacturer of putting gas into the crisp bag.

6 When a new television is purchased there is often a small bag of silica gel inside the cardboard carton.

(a) What is the purpose of the silica gel?
(b) From time to time the silica gel is heated in the oven. What is the purpose of heating the silica gel?

(c) Sometimes a small amount of cobalt(II) chloride is added to the silica gel. Explain the purpose of the cobalt(II) chloride.

7 It is suggested that a new packaging material would be better for packaging biscuits than existing materials. Give three properties that this material should have if it is to be suitable.

8 Fig. 9.2 shows a beaker containing concentrated sulphuric acid before and after standing exposed to the atmosphere for one week.

(a) What change can be observed after one week?
(b) Explain why this change took place.
(c) What does this experiment tell you about concentrated sulphuric acid?

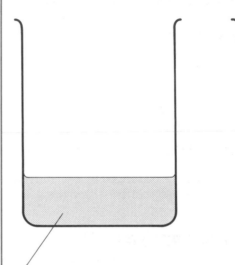

concentrated sulphuric acid

before   after

Fig. 9.2 Concentrated sulphuric acid exposed to the atmosphere for one week

Summary

Chemicals often change on exposure to the atmosphere. These changes may involve the reaction of the substance with oxygen, carbon dioxide or water vapour.

Deliquescent substances absorb water vapour from the atmosphere and dissolve in the absorbed water. Common deliquescent substances include lithium chloride, iron(III) chloride, copper(II) nitrate, zinc nitrate, calcium nitrate and anyhdrous calcium chloride.

Hygroscopic substances only absorb small amounts of water vapour. Common examples include sodium chloride, copper(II) oxide, anhydrous copper(II) sulphate and anhydrous sodium carbonate.

Efflorescent substances lose water of crystallization on exposure to the atmosphere. Common examples include sodium carbonate crystals, sodium sulphate crystals and sodium tetraborate (borax).

Unit 10

Atoms and their structure

In Foundation Skills – Chemistry *Volume 2 Unit 2 it was explained that all elements are made up of tiny particles called atoms. A cube of iron (2 cm × 2 cm × 2 cm) contains about 60 000 000 000 000 000 000 000 atoms of iron. Each atom of iron has a diameter of about 0.000 000 1 mm and a mass of about 0.000 000 000 000 000 000 000 09 g.*

Much of the credit for our understanding of atoms is given to John Dalton (1766 – 1844). He proposed that all atoms are similar to billiard balls – hard, solid and impossible to divide. In this Unit we are going to consider the structure of atoms, i.e. what they are made up from.

10.1 Protons, neutrons and electrons

All atoms are made up from three basic particles called protons, neutrons and electrons. An iron atom is different from a copper atom because it contains different numbers of these particles.

Proton A proton (abbreviation p) is a small positively charged particle. Its mass is said to be 1 a.m.u. (1 **atomic mass unit** – a useful unit for the mass of protons, neutrons and electrons).

Electron An electron (e) is much smaller than a proton or neutron. Two thousand electrons would have approximately the same mass as a proton or neutron. An electron has a single negative charge.

Neutron A neutron (n) is a particle which has approximately the same mass as a proton but it has no charge – it is neutral.

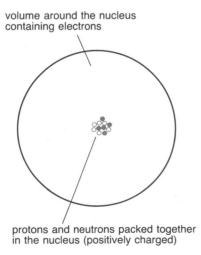

Fig. 10.1 Arrangement of protons, neutrons and electrons in an atom

volume around the nucleus containing electrons

protons and neutrons packed together in the nucleus (positively charged)

The properties of the three particles are summarized in Table 10.1.

Particle	Approximate mass	Charge
Proton(p)	1 a.m.u.	+1
Neutron(n)	1 a.m.u.	0
Electron(e)	negligible	−1

Table 10.1 Properties of protons, neutrons and electrons

All atoms are neutral. They must, therefore, contain equal numbers of protons and electrons.

10.2 Atomic number and mass number

Atomic number (Z) and **mass number** (A) are two 'vital statistics' for any atom. The atomic number is the number of protons in an atom. The mass number is the total number of protons and neutrons in the atom.

If you are given the atomic number and mass number for an atom, you should be able to work out the number of protons, neutrons and electrons the atom contains.

For example a phosphorus atom has an atomic number of 15 and a mass number of 31. It is sometimes represented as $^{31}_{15}P$.

The phosphorus atom contains
15 protons (because the atomic number is 15)
15 electrons (because an atom contains equal numbers of protons and electrons)
and 16 neutrons (mass number – atomic number)

10.3 Arrangement of protons, neutrons and electrons

In any atom the protons and neutrons are tightly packed together in the **nucleus** (Fig. 10.1). The nucleus is positively charged.

The electrons move around the nucleus at high speeds in certain **shells** or **energy levels**. Each shell can only contain up to a maximum number of electrons (Fig. 10.2)

Fig. 10.3 shows simple two-dimensional diagrams of some atoms.

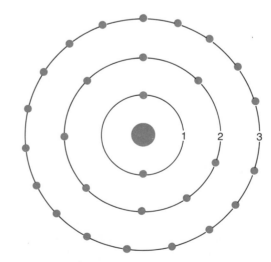

Fig. 10.2 Maximum number of electrons in shells 1, 2 and 3

52

Fig. 10.3 Simple diagrams of some atoms

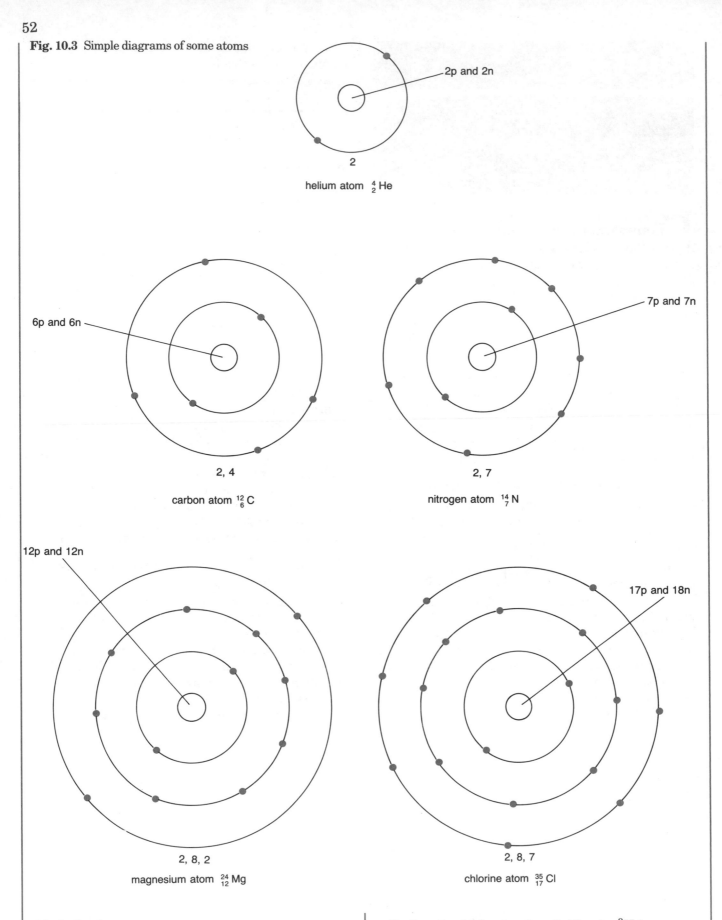

2p and 2n

2

helium atom $^4_2$He

6p and 6n

2, 4

carbon atom $^{12}_6$C

7p and 7n

2, 7

nitrogen atom $^{14}_7$N

12p and 12n

2, 8, 2

magnesium atom $^{24}_{12}$Mg

17p and 18n

2, 8, 7

chlorine atom $^{35}_{17}$Cl

10.4 Isotopes

It is sometimes possible to get different atoms of the same element. These are called **isotopes**.

For example, there are three isotopes of hydrogen.

Normal hydrogen atom $-^1_1$H (see Fig. 10.4)

Heavy hydrogen atom (sometimes called deuterium) $-^2_1$H (see Fig. 10.5)

Radioactive hydrogen atom (tritium) $-^3_1$H (see Fig. 10.6)

All three atoms are hydrogen atoms because they contain one electron and one proton. They do, however, contain different numbers of neutrons. All three isotopes of hydrogen have the same chemical properties.

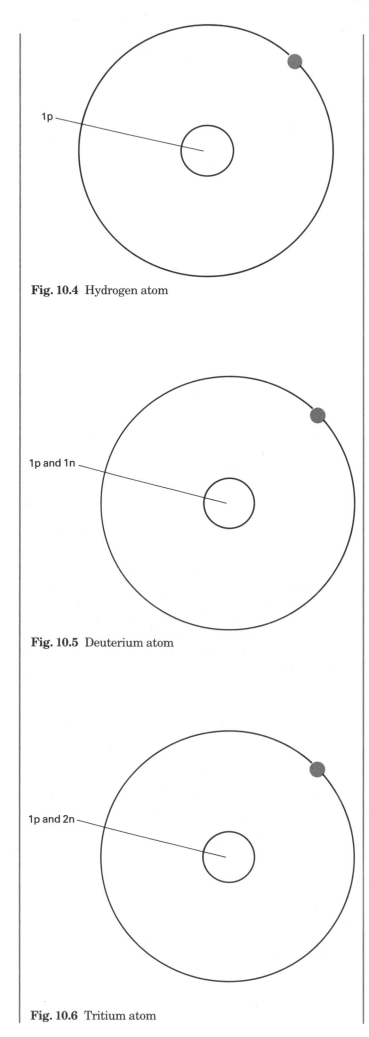

Fig. 10.4 Hydrogen atom

1p and 1n

Fig. 10.5 Deuterium atom

1p and 2n

Fig. 10.6 Tritium atom

Activities

Atom	Mass number	Atomic number	Number of p	n	e
A	16		8		
B		7		7	
C	19	9			
D				9	8
E			6	8	

Table 10.2 Complete the table for atoms A to E

1 Complete Table 10.2 giving the numbers of particles in the 5 atoms labelled A – E.
Which of the atoms A – E in Table 10.2 are isotopes of the same element?
2 Fig. 10.7 shows a simple representation of an atom.
Write down the:

(i) number of protons present;
(ii) number of electrons present;
(iii) number of neutrons present;
(iv) atomic number of the atom;
(v) mass number of the atom;
(vi) arrangement of electrons in the atom.

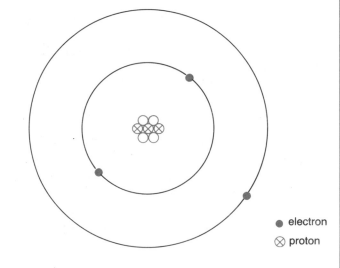

● electron
⊗ proton

Fig. 10.7 Answer question 2 about this atom

Summary

Atoms are made up from three particles called protons (p), neutrons(n) and electrons(e).

The protons and neutrons are tightly packed in the positively charged nucleus. The electrons travel around the nucleus in shells. Each shell can hold only a maximum number of electrons.

Unit 11

Ions and electrolysis

Atoms are neutral because they contain equal numbers of protons and electrons. If an atom loses one or more electrons it becomes positively charged. If it gains electrons it becomes negatively charged.

An atom which has gained or lost electrons is called an **ion**. A positively charged ion formed by losing electrons is sometimes called a **cation**, and a negatively charged ion formed by gaining electrons is called an **anion**.

In general, metals lose electrons and form positive ions and non-metals gain electrons and form negative ions.

Ion formation always involves gain and loss of electrons – never protons or neutrons.

Some examples of ions

Na^+ Sodium ion formed when a sodium atom loses 1 electron
Pb^{2+} Lead ion formed when a lead atom loses 2 electrons
Al^{3+} Aluminium ion formed when an aluminium atom loses 3 electrons
Br^- Bromide ion formed when a bromine atom gains 1 electron
O^{2-} Oxide ion formed when an oxygen atom gains 2 electrons

In *Foundation Skills – Chemistry* Volume 2 Unit 11 an introduction to electrolysis is considered. Electrolysis is the splitting up of a substance with electricity. Ions are important in the understanding of electrolysis.

11.1 Electrolysis of molten lead(II) bromide

Fig. 11.1 shows apparatus suitable for the electrolysis of lead(II) bromide.

Lead(II) bromide is a white solid at room temperature. It contains Pb^{2+} and Br^- ions.

No electrolysis takes place while the lead(II) bromide is solid. In the solid the ions are not free to move. On melting the structure breaks down and the ions are free to move or migrate.

The positive lead ions (Pb^{2+}) move towards the negative electrode (cathode) and the negative bromide ions (Br^-) move towards the positive electrode (anode).

At the electrodes the ions are discharged and the products, lead and bromine, are formed. The cathode is negatively charged because it has a surplus of

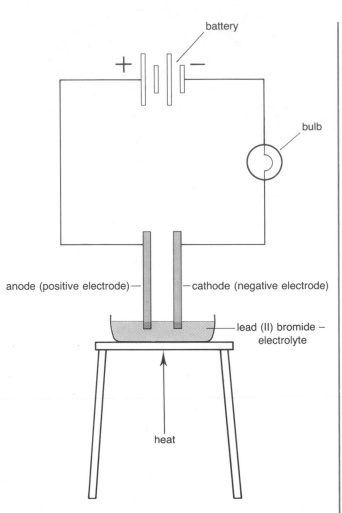

Fig. 11.1 Apparatus for electrolysis of lead (II) bromide

electrons and the anode is positively charged because it is short of electrons. This redistribution of electrons is brought about by the battery. The discharging of ions at the electrodes involves the transfer of electrons. At the cathode electrons are transferred from the cathode to the lead ions. Lead is produced at the cathode.

$$Pb^{2+} + 2e \rightarrow Pb$$

At the anode electrons are taken from the bromide ions and given to the electrode. Bromine is formed.

$$2\,Br^- \rightarrow Br_2 + 2e$$

11.2 Electrolysis of aqueous solutions

An aqueous solution is a solution in which the solvent is water. An aqueous solution of sodium chloride contains sodium Na^+ and chloride Cl^- ions. In addition to these ions, there are ions present from the splitting up of water molecules.

$$H_2O \rightarrow H^+ + OH^-$$

The products of the electrolysis of an aqueous solution can be explained in terms of discharge of ions in a similar way.

Anode

$$2Cl^- \rightarrow Cl_2 + 2e$$

Cathode

$$2H^+ + 2e \rightarrow H_2$$

Activities

1 Fig. 11.2 shows simple diagrams of lithium, oxygen and fluorine atoms.
Draw simple diagrams of Li^+, O^{2-} and F^- ions.

2 Complete Table 11.1 which gives the products of the electrolysis of a number of aqueous solutions. Why are the products of the electrolysis different for dilute and concentrated solutions of copper(II) chloride?

3 Potassium chromate contains yellow coloured ions with a negative charge.

A drop of potassium chromate solution is placed at the centre of a piece of filter paper strip moistened with salt solution.

Two wires from a battery are connected to opposite ends of the filter paper (Fig. 11.3)

(a) What would be observed if:
 (i) the apparatus was left set up for some time;
 (ii) the filter paper had been moistened with pure water rather than salt solution?
In each case explain your answer.

(b) The experiment was repeated using a drop of green copper(II) chromate solution in place of potassium chromate solution. Copper(II) chromate contains blue Cu^{2+} and yellow CrO_4^{2-} ions.
What would be observed during the experiment?

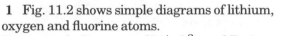

Fig. 11.2 Lithium, oxygen and fluorine atoms

Explain your answer.

(c) This method of separating coloured ions on a piece of paper is called electrophoresis. Which method of separating coloured dyes, without using electricity, might be confused with electrophoresis?

Solution of	Ions present	Product at the cathode	anode	Ion discharged at the cathode	anode
Zinc sulphate	$Zn^{2+}, SO_4^{2-}, H^+, OH^-$	zinc	oxygen	Zn^{2+}	OH^-
Sodium hydroxide	Na^+, OH^-, H^+	hydrogen	oxygen		
Sodium sulphate				H^+	OH^-
Silver nitrate	Ag^+, NO_3^-, H^+, OH^-			Ag^+	OH^-
Calcium nitrate	$Ca^{2+}, NO_3^-, H^+, OH^-$	hydrogen	oxygen		
Very dilute soln. of copper(II) chloride	Cu^{2+}, Cl^-, H^+, OH^-		oxygen	Cu^{2+}	
Concentrated soln. of copper(II) chloride			chlorine	Cu^{2+}	

Table 11.1 Products of electrolysis of aqueous solutions

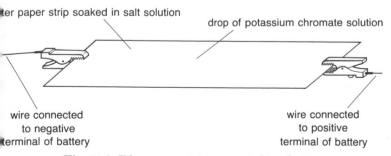
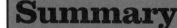

Fig. 11.3 Filter paper strip connected to a battery

Summary

If atoms gain or lose electrons they form ions. Metals lose electrons and form positively charged ions. Non-metals gain electrons and form negatively charged ions.

Electrolysis can be explained in terms of the movement and discharge of ions.

Unit 12

The Periodic Table

At the beginning of the nineteenth century a large number of elements was discovered and chemists were looking for similarities between these new elements and existing elements.

Döbereiner (1829) suggested that elements could be grouped in threes called triads. Each member of a triad has similar properties, for example:

lithium, **sodium** and **potassium**;
chlorine, **bromine** and **iodine**;
iron, **cobalt** and **nickel**.

Newlands (1863) arranged the elements in order of increasing atomic mass. He noticed that there was some similarity between each eighth element.

Li Be B C N O F
Na Mg Al Si P S Cl etc

	I	II											III	IV	V	VI	VII	0
1							1 H Hydrogen 1											4 He Helium 2
2	7 Li Lithium 3	9 Be Beryllium 4											11 B Boron 5	12 C Carbon 6	14 N Nitrogen 7	16 O Oxygen 8	19 F Fluorine 9	20 Ne Neon 10
3	23 Na Sodium 11	24 Mg Magnesium 12					Transition Elements						27 Al Aluminium 13	28 Si Silicon 14	31 P Phosphorus 15	32 S Sulphur 16	35.5 Cl Chlorine 17	40 Ar Argon 18
4	39 K Potassium 19	40 Ca Calcium 20	45 Sc Scandium 21	48 Ti Titanium 22	51 V Vanadium 23	52 Cr Chromium 24	55 Mn Manganese 25	56 Fe Iron 26	59 Co Cobalt 27	59 Ni Nickel 28	64 Cu Copper 29	65 Zn Zinc 30	70 Ga Gallium 31	73 Ge Germanium 32	75 As Arsenic 33	79 Se Selenium 34	80 Br Bromine 35	84 Kr Krypton 36
	85.5 Rb Rubidium 37	88 Sr Strontium 38	89 Y Yttrium 39	91 Zr Zirconium 40	93 Nb Niobium 41	96 Mo Molybdenum 42	98 Tc Technetium 43	101 Ru Ruthenium 44	103 Rh Rhodium 45	106 Pd Palladium 46	108 Ag Silver 47	112 Cd Cadmium 48	115 In Indium 49	119 Sn Tin 50	122 Sb Antimony 51	128 Te Tellurium 52	127 I Iodine 53	131 Xe Xenon 54
	133 Cs Caesium 55	137 Ba Barium 56	139 La Lanthanum 57	178.5 Hf Hafnium 72	181 Ta Tantalum 73	184 W Tungsten 74	186 Re Rhenium 75	190 Os Osmium 76	192 Ir Iridium 77	195 Pt Platinum 78	197 Au Gold 79	201 Hg Mercury 80	204 Tl Thallium 81	207 Pb Lead 82	209 Bi Bismuth 83	210 Po Polonium 84	210 At Astatine 85	222 Rn Radon 86
	223 Fr Francium 87	226 Ra Radium 88	227 Ac Actinium 89															

Key

Atomic Mass
Symbol
Name
Atomic Number

139 La Lanthanum 57	140 Ce Cerium 58	141 Pr Praseodymium 59	144 Nd Neodymium 60	147 Pm Promethium 61	150 Sm Samarium 62	152 Eu Europium 63	157 Gd Gadolinium 64	159 Tb Terbium 65	162.5 Dy Dysprosium 66	165 Ho Holmium 67	167 Er Erbium 68	169 Tm Thulium 69	173 Yb Ytterbium 70	175 Lu Lutetium 71
227 Ac Actinium 89	232 Th Thorium 90	231 Pa Protactinium 91	238 U Uranium 92	237 Np Neptunium 93	242 Pu Plutonium 94	243 Am Americium 95	247 Cm Curium 96	247 Bk Berkelium 97	251 Cf Californium 98	254 Es Einsteinium 99	253 Fm Fermium 100	256 Md Mendeleevium 101	254 No Nobelium 102	257 Lw Lawrencium 103

Fig. 12.1 The Periodic Table

Period	I	II											III	IV	V	VI	VII	
1							1 H 1											2 He 2
2	2,1 Li 3	2,2 Be 4											2,3 B 5	2,4 C 6	2,5 N 7	2,6 O 8	2,7 F 9	2,8 Ne 10
3	2,8,1 Na 11	2,8,2 Mg 12											2,8,3 Al 13	2,8,4 Si 14	2,8,5 P 15	2,8,6 S 16	2,8,7 Cl 17	2,8,8 Ar 18
4	2,8,8,1 K 19	2,8,8,2 Ca 20	2,8,9,2 Sc 21	2,8,10,2 Ti 22	2,8,11,2 V 23	2,8,13,1 Cr 24	2,8,13,2 Mn 25	2,8,14,2 Fe 26	2,8,15,2 Co 27	2,8,16,2 Ni 28	2,8,18,1 Cu 29	2,8,18,2 Zn 30	2,8,18,3 Ga 31	2,8,18,4 Ge 32	2,8,18,5 As 33	2,8,18,6 Se 34	2,8,18,7 Br 35	2,8,18,8 Kr 36

Fig. 12.2 The first 36 elements of the Periodic Table

These were called Newlands' Octaves and he stressed a similarity with music. Unfortunately the pattern broke down with the heavier elements and because he had not left gaps for undiscovered elements. His work did not receive much support at the time although we now know that he was close to something tremendous.

In 1869 the Russian chemist Dmitri Mendeléef arranged the elements in order of increasing atomic mass but took into account the patterns of behaviour of the known elements. He found it necessary to leave gaps where elements were not known at that time. His table enabled him to predict the properties of gallium and germanium although they were not known. The Periodic Table we use today closely resembles the table drawn up by Mendeléef.

A modification of the Periodic Table was made following the work of Rutherford and Moseley. It was realized that the elements should be arranged in order of atomic number, i.e. the number of protons in the nucleus.

12.1 The modern Periodic Table

The Periodic Table is an arrangement of the elements in order of increasing atomic number with elements having similar properties in the same vertical column (or group). The horizontal rows are called periods.

The Periodic Table is shown in Fig. 12.1. The main block elements are shaded and between the two parts of the main block are the transition metals.

The bold zig-zag line divides the metals on the left-hand side of the line from non-metals on the right-hand side.

The elements that are gases at room temperature and pressure are towards the top on the right-hand side of the Periodic Table.

In Units 13–18 different groups of elements or individual elements will be considered but in each case reference will be made back to the position or positions of elements in the Periodic Table.

12.2 Relationship between atomic structure and the Periodic Table

Fig. 12.2 shows the first 36 elements in the Periodic Table and the arrangement of electrons in these elements.

You will notice that:

1 Elements in the same vertical group have the same number of electrons in the outer shell. All of the elements in group I have one electron on the outer shell.

2 The number of electrons in the outer shell is the same as the group in which the element is placed. Carbon is in group IV and has four electrons in its outer shell.

3 An element in period 3, for example, has electrons in the first three shells.

The chemical properties of an element depend very much upon the arrangement of electrons in the atom and this is related to the position of the element in the Periodic Table.

Activities

1 Read the following biographies and answer the questions which follow.

John Alexander Newlands (1837–1898)

Newlands studied under A.W. von Hofmann at the Royal College of Chemistry in London. Later he became assistant to J.T. Way, chemist to the Royal Agricultural Society.

He set up himself as a consultant analyst with his brother in 1864 but the venture quickly failed. In 1866 he became chemist in a sugar factory in the Victoria Docks, London.

About 1860, through the work of Cannizzaro and others, lists of accurate atomic weights for the elements were being made. Newlands was the first to point out, in papers published from 1863, that if the elements were arranged in order of increasing atomic weight, similar properties tended to appear every eighth element. For this reason his idea became known as the Law of Octaves.

Newlands published his ideas in the form of a table of about sixty elements in 1865 and a year later he spoke to the Chemical Society about his work. Unfortunately his work was ahead of its time and his lecture was received with scepticism and even ridicule. The Chemical Society refused to publish his papers. It was not until Mendeléef's work was published in 1869 that Newland's work received recognition.

Later Newland's work was formally recognized by the Royal Society which awarded him the Davy Medal in 1887. He was never, however, elected as a Fellow.

Activities continued

Dmitri Ivanovich Mendeléef (1834–1907)

Mendeléef was born in Tobolsk in Siberia in 1834. He was the fourteenth, and last, child of the Director of the Gymnasium at Tobolsk. When Mendeléef was 16 his father retired early through blindness and he was taken by his mother to St. Petersburg (now called Leningrad) to seek higher education. He trained as a teacher there and after training was sent to Odessa. In 1856 he returned to St. Petersburg and took a degree in Chemistry.

In 1859, after graduation, he went for further training to Paris and Heidelberg. In 1861 he returned to St. Petersburg as Professor of Chemistry. He resigned his university appointment in 1890 following an internal dispute with the Minister of Education. In 1893 he became Director of the Bureau of Weights and Measures and held this post until his death.

He was in conflict with authority many times throughout his life. He was in dispute for a long time with the Church because his second marriage was technically bigamous.

Mendeléef was a prolific writer and wrote over 300 books and papers. Most were chemical but he also wrote on the subjects of art, education and economics. In 1868 he started his great text book called in English 'Principles of Chemistry'. While doing this he considered classifying the elements and suggested the 'Periodic Law'. He presented this paper to the Russian Chemical Society in October 1868. His work was carried out in complete ignorance of the work of Newlands in London.

His great discoveries leading to the Periodic Table were warmly welcomed. He was awarded the Davy medal in 1882 and the Copley medal in 1905 by the Royal Society. He was elected Foreign Minister in 1890.

Without doubt Mendeléef was one of the great chemists of the nineteenth century.

(a) Compare the reception of the work of Mendeléef and Newlands by chemists of their time.
(b) Which famous chemist and teacher was partly responsible for the enthusiasm that Newlands showed for Chemistry? (See *Foundation Skills — Chemistry* Volume 3 Unit 1.)
(c) What advantages do chemists have today when carrying out research?

```
                                    Ti=50      Zr=90      ?=1?
                                    V=51       Nb=94      Ta=1?
                                    Cr=52      Mo=96      W=1?
                                    Mn=55      Rh=104,4   Pt=19?
                                    Fe=56      Ru=104,4   Ir=19?
                              Ni=Co=59         Pl=106?,   Os=19?
      H=1
                                    Cu=63,4    Ag=108     Hg=2?
          Be=9,4   Mg=24    Zn=65,2   Cd=112
          B=11     Al=27,4  ?=68      Ur=116   Au=19?
          C=12     Si=28    ?=70      Sn=118
          N=14     P=31     As=75     Sb=122   Bi=21?
          O=16     S=32     Se=79,4   Te=128?
          F=19     Cl=35,5  Br=80     I=127
  Li=7   Na=23     K=39     Rb=85,4   Cs=133   Tl=2?
                   Ca=40    Sr=?7,?   Ba=137   Pb=2?
                   ?=45     Ce=92
                   ?Er=56   La=94
                   ?Yt=60   Di=95
                   ?In=75,6 Th=118?
```

Fig. 12.3 An old Periodic Table

*2 Making a Periodic Table

Table 12.1 lists some of the elements known to
Mendeléef and some of the properties of these
elements. Make some cards – one for each
element – like the one shown in Fig. 12.4. Use
different coloured felt pens or coloured pencils for
writing on the cards with the colours indicated on the
table.

(a) Arrange the cards in order of increasing relative
atomic mass. What do you notice about the atomic
numbers?

(b) Now keeping the order the same, arrange the
cards in rows but keep cards written in the same
colour in the same vertical column.

(c) Obviously Mendeléef's table was much larger. He
had information on about 60 elements.

There are obviously gaps in your table, as there
were gaps in Mendeléef's table. He was able to predict
the properties of missing elements very accurately.
Table 12.2 gives some information about elements not
known by Mendeléef. Make cards for these elements
and put them into your table.

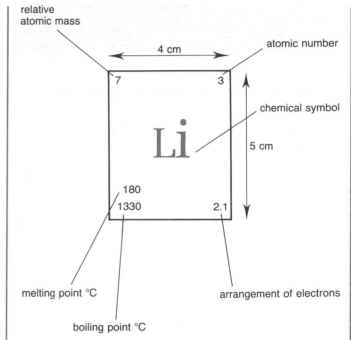

Fig. 12.4 Make cards for the elements from Table 12.1

Colour of ink	Element	Relative atomic mass	Atomic number	Melting point °C	Boiling point °C	Arrangement of electrons
1	Aluminium Al	27	13	660	2060	2,8,3
2	Arsenic As	75	33		615	2,8,18,5
3	Beryllium Be	9	4	1280	2700	2,2
1	Boron B	11	5	2000	3000	2,3
4	Bromine Br	80	35	−7	58	2,8,18,7
3	Calcium Ca	40	20	850	1440	2,8,8,2
5	Carbon C	12	6		4200	2,4
4	Chlorine Cl	35.5	17	−101	−35	2,8,7
7	Lithium Li	7	3	180	1330	2,1
3	Magnesium Mg	24	12	650	1110	2,8,2
2	Nitrogen N	14	7	−210	−196	2,5
6	Oxygen O	16	8	−219	−183	2,6
2	Phosphorus P	31	15	44	280	2,8,5
7	Potassium K	39	19	64	760	2,8,8,1
6	Selenium Se	79	34	217	690	2,8,18,6
5	Silicon Si	28	14	1410	2700	2,8,4
7	Sodium Na	23	11	98	890	2,8,1
6	Sulphur S	32	16	119	445	2,8,6

Table 12.1 Some elements known to Mendeléef and their properties

Colour of ink	Element	Relative atomic mass	Atomic number	Melting point °C	Boiling point °C	Arrangement of electrons
8	Argon Ar	40	18	−189	−189	2,8,8
4	Fluorine F	19	9	−220	−188	2,7
1	Gallium Ga	70	31	30	2200	2,8,18,3
5	Germanium Ge	72.5	32	950	2800	2,8,18,4
8	Helium He	4	2	−259	−253	2
8	Krypton Kr	84	36	−157	−153	2,8,18,8
8	Neon Ne	20	10	−249	−246	2,8

Table 12.2 Elements not known to Mendeléef

Activities continued

Colour of ink	Element	Relative atomic mass	Atomic number	Melting point °C	Boiling point °C	Arrangement of electrons
9	Cobalt Co	59	27	1490	2900	2,8,15,2
9	Copper Cu	63.5	29	1080	2500	2,8,18,1
9	Chromium Cr	52	24	1900	2500	2,8,12,2
9	Iron Fe	56	26	1540	3000	2,8,14,2
9	Manganese Mn	55	25	1250	2000	2,8,13,2
9	Nickel Ni	59	28	1450	2800	2,8,16,2
9	Scandium Sc	45	21	1400	2500	2,8,9,2
9	Titanium Ti	48	22	1670	3300	2,8,10,2
9	Vanadium V	51	23	1900	3400	2,8,11,2
9	Zinc Zn	65.5	30	419	910	2,8,18,2

Table 12.3 The first row of transition metals

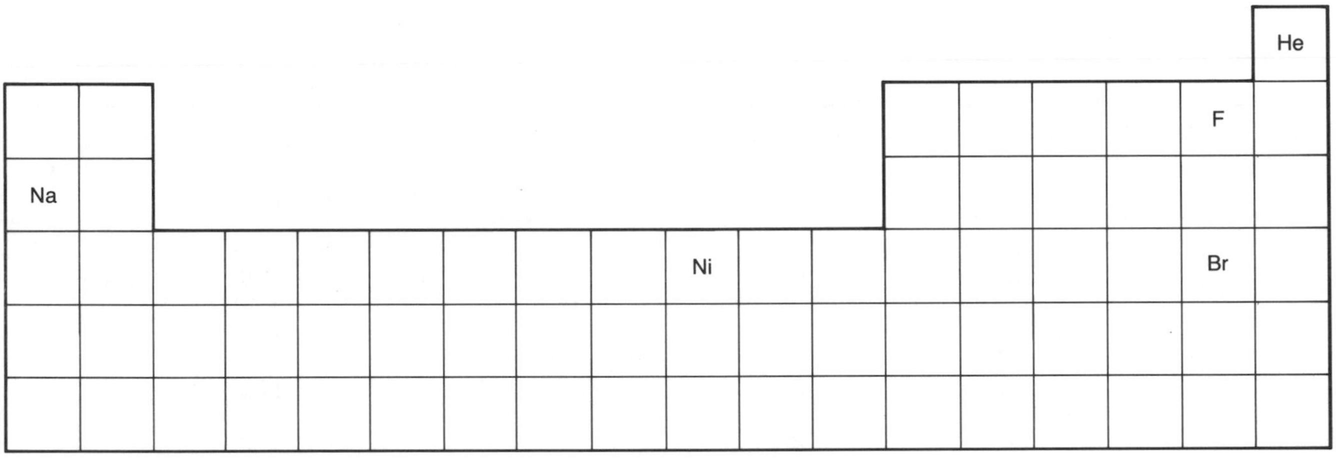

Fig. 12.5 Skeleton Periodic Table

(d) Table 12.3 gives information about the first row of transition metals. Put these elements into your table. Find two elements which seem to be out of place if you look only at the relative atomic masses.

(e) What patterns can you see in each row and column of the Periodic Table you have made in

(i) arrangement of electrons;

(ii) melting point;

(iii) boiling point?

3 Fig. 12.5 shows a skeleton Periodic Table with only some of the elements inserted.

Using only the elements in Fig. 12.5, give the symbols for the:

(i) two elements in the same period;

(ii) two elements in the same group;

(iii) alkali metal element;

(iv) non-metal liquid at room temperature;

(v) transition metal;

(vi) noble gas;

(vii) metal usually stored under oil;

(viii) element whose atoms contain the greatest number of protons;

(ix) halogen atom which is a gas at room temperature;

(x) element which would contain the greatest number of atoms in a 10 g sample.

Summary

The Periodic Table is an arrangement of elements in order of increasing atomic number with elements having similar properties in the same vertical column. The horizontal rows are called periods and the vertical columns are called groups.

Unit 13

The Alkali Metals

The elements in group 1 of the Periodic Table are called the alkali metals. These elements include:

Lithium   Li
Sodium   Na
Potassium K

The elements rubidium Rb, caesium Cs and francium Fr are also alkali metals but are rare.

13.1 Appearance of the alkali metals

Alkali metals are bought as solid lumps which are kept under paraffin oil. This is to prevent them reacting with water vapour, oxygen and carbon dioxide in the air which would be dangerous.

If a lump of lithium, sodium or potassium is required it should be removed from the bottle with a pair of tongs and placed on a clean, dry china tile.

Alkali metals are soft and they can be cut easily with a knife. For reasons of safety, only small pieces of alkali metals should be used. The surface of the metal produced on cutting is shiny and silvery. It quickly loses its shine, however, as the metal reacts with the air.

Alkali metals are good conductors of electricity.

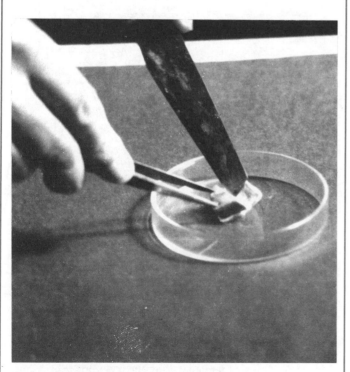

Fig. 13.1 Cutting sodium with a knife

13.2 Reactions of alkali metals with air or oxygen

A small piece of lithium burns brightly when heated producing white smoke and leaving a white residue. This residue is lithium oxide. The reaction can be represented by the word equation:

lithium + oxygen (from the air) → lithium oxide

If the residue is tested with universal indicator, the indicator turns purple (pH 12) showing that a strong alkali has been formed.

Similar reactions occur if pieces of sodium and potassium are heated in air or oxygen.

sodium + oxygen → sodium oxide
potassium + oxygen → potassium oxide

13.3 Reactions of alkali metals with cold water

Lithium reacts slowly with water producing bubbles of a colourless gas. The gas can be collected in a test tube (Fig. 13.2). The gas burns with a squeaky pop when a lighted splint is put into the gas. The gas is hydrogen. The resulting solution contains lithium hydroxide which is an alkali.

lithium + water → lithium hydroxide + hydrogen

Similar reactions occur with sodium and potassium. The reaction of sodium is faster than the reaction of lithium.

sodium + water → sodium hydroxide + hydrogen

Potassium reacts faster than sodium. The hydrogen produced catches alight and burns with a pinkish flame.

potassium + water → potassium hydroxide + hydrogen

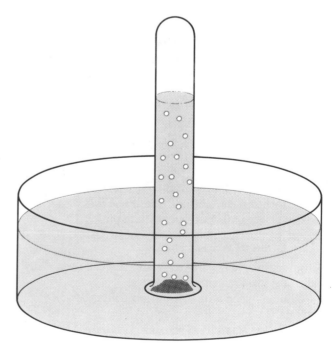

Fig. 13.2 Collecting hydrogen from the reaction of lithium with cold water

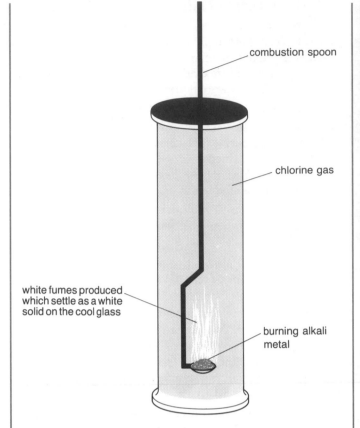

Fig. 13.3 The burning of lithium in chlorine

Fig. 13.4 Sodium street lights

13.4 Reactions of alkali metals with chlorine

Lithium burns in chlorine to form lithium chloride (Fig. 13.3).

lithium + chlorine → lithium chloride

Sodium and potassium react with chlorine in a similar way.

sodium + chlorine → sodium chloride
potassium + chlorine → potassium chloride

13.5 Alkali metal compounds

Alkali metals are reactive metals and form a whole range of compounds. These compounds have various properties in common.

1 Most compounds are white in colour – exception potassium manganate(VII).
2 Most compounds are soluble in water.
3 Alkali metals are not easily decomposed on heating.
4 Alkali metal compounds colour a Bunsen burner flame. Lithium compounds colour the flame red, sodium orange and potassium lilac-pink.

13.6 Uses of alkali metals

Alkali metals do not have a wide range of uses. Only sodium is used in large quantities.

Sodium is used as a coolant in nuclear power stations.

Sodium gas is used in street lights. These lights give a bright orange coloured light.

Sodium is used to extract expensive metals such as titanium from their ores.

Fig. 13.5 Mr Jones demonstrating the reaction of potassium with water

Activities

1 Fig. 13.5 shows Mr Jones demonstrating the reactions of potassium with cold water.
List any possible dangers in the demonstration.

Alkali metal	Atomic number	Melting point °C	Boiling point °C	Density g per cm³	Formula of chloride	Formula of oxide
Lithium	7	180	1330	0.53	LiCl	Li_2O
Sodium	11	98	890	0.97	NaCl	Na_2O
Potassium	19	64	760	0.86	KCl	K_2O
Rubidium	37	39	700	1.5	RbCl	Rb_2O
Caesium	55	29	650	1.9	CsCl	Cs_2O

Table 13.1 Properties of the alkali metals

2 Table 13.1 gives the properties of the alkali metals lithium, sodium, potassium, rubidium and caesium. Use this information to answer the questions which follow.

(a) Which alkali metal in Table 13.1:
  (i) has the highest melting point;
 (ii) has the lowest boiling point;
(iii) has a density which does not fit into the pattern of the group;
 (iv) has the greatest density;
  (v) would float on water but sink in a liquid with a density of 0.9 g per cm³;

 (vi) has atoms which contain the least number of protons?

(b) Plot the boiling points of lithium, sodium, potassium, caesium and rubidium on the graph in Fig. 13.6.
Draw a smooth curve through the points you have plotted. From your graph make an estimate of the boiling point of francium (atomic number 87).

(c) Predict the following for the element francium:
  (i) melting point;
 (ii) density;
(iii) formula of francium chloride;
 (iv) formula of francium oxide.

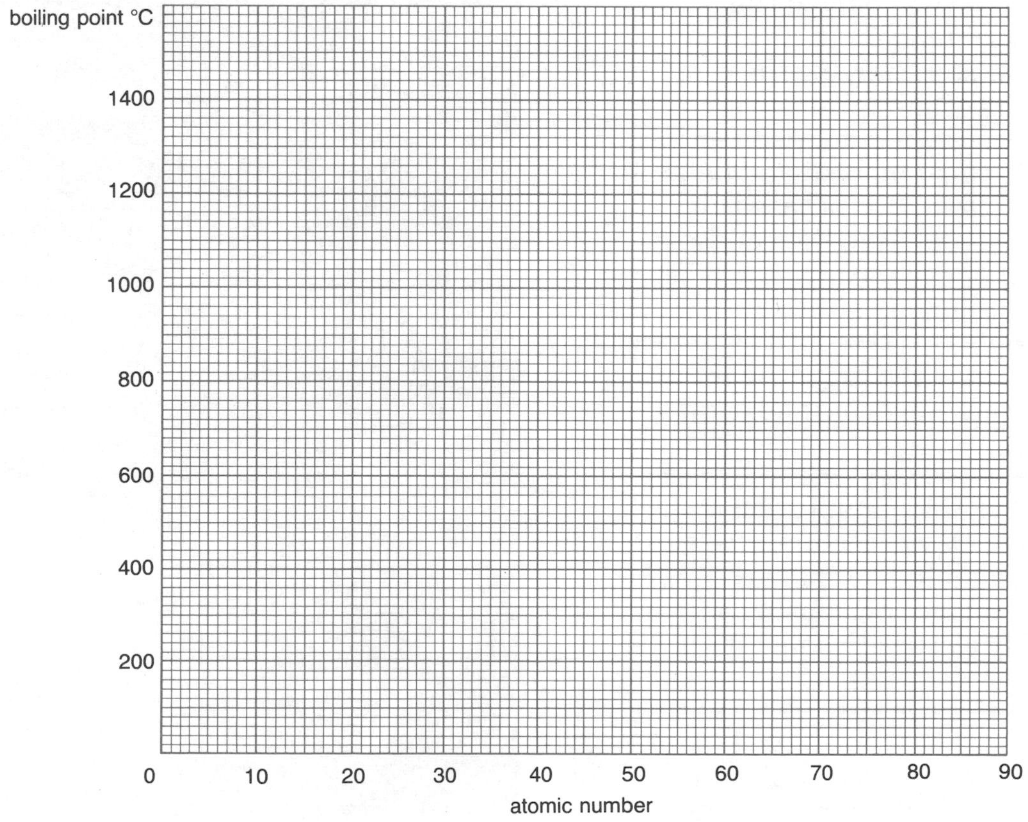

boiling point °C

atomic number

Fig. 13.6 Plot the boiling points of the alkali metals

Activities

3 Read the following account of the life of Humphrey Davy and answer the questions which follow.

(a) Name three elements discovered by Davy.
(b) Rearrange the following letters to find the name of one of Davy's famous assistants.

ARFDYAA

Humphrey Davy (1778–1829)

Humphrey Davy was born in Penzance in 1778. His father was a woodcarver. He attended Penzance Grammar School but was not a good student!

When he left school at fifteen his father died and he had to support his mother and four other children. He became apprenticed to a surgeon. He started to educate himself and to develop his interest in poetry.

Davy started to be interested in Chemistry at the age of 19. He showed particular interest in the work of Lavoisier. After only three months' study, Davy wrote his first chemical paper.

At the age of 19 he was offered the position of superintendent at a laboratory in Bristol studying the medicinal effects of gases.

In 1799 Davy's paper on heat and light was widely criticized. It was based on little experiment and from then on Davy made sure that all his theories could be justified by experiment.

Davy demonstrated the properties of nitrous oxide (laughing gas) and showed its use as an anaesthetic.

He moved to the Royal Institution in London in 1801. Davy's lectures were extremely popular and he showed tremendous brilliance and dash. He started to study electricity again in 1806.

In 1807 he carried out the electrolysis of potash using, not a solution, but some barely moist solid. Where the platinum electrode was in contact with the potash small blobs of silvery metal were formed which burnt in air. Within three days of obtaining potassium from potash, he had extracted sodium from caustic soda. Later, following a serious illness, he extracted barium and strontium by electrolysis.

Davy married a rich widow in 1812 who was a cousin of Sir Walter Scott. He was knighted by the Prince Regent and was President of the Royal Society for some years.

He invented a miner's safety lamp which saved the lives of many miners. The lamp was based on the principle that an inflammable gas will only burn on one side of a wire gauze and not through it.

Scientific Researches! — New Discoveries in PNEUMATICKS! — or — an Experimental Lecture on the Powers of Air

(a)

(b)

Fig. 13.7 (a) Lecture demonstration at the Royal Institution – Davy is the young man assisting with the experiment
(b) Miner's safety lamp

Summary

The alkali metal family is in group I of the Periodic Table. It includes the elements lithium, sodium and potassium.

From the reactions with water, in particular, it is possible to conclude that reactivity increases down the group, that is:

lithium is less reactive than sodium which is less reactive than potassium.

Unit 14

The halogens

T*he halogens are a family of non-metallic elements in group VII of the Periodic Table.*

The elements in the family are:

Fluorine   F
Chlorine   Cl
Bromine   Br
Iodine   I

Astatine At is also a member of the family but it is very rare. It is radioactive.

14.1 Appearance of halogen elements

Fluorine and chlorine are gases at room temperature and pressure. Fluorine is colourless and chlorine is greenish-yellow. Bromine is a dark red liquid. Iodine is a shiny dark grey solid.

14.2 Reactions of halogens with metals

The word 'halogen' means salt-producer. All halogens react with metals to form salts. Fluorine reacts with metals to form fluorides, chlorine forms chlorides, bromine forms bromides and iodine forms iodides.

Fig. 14.1 shows apparatus for carrying out the reaction of iron with dry chlorine. On heating the iron, a glow spreads through the iron as an exothermic reaction takes place. Anhydrous iron(III) chloride sublimes and is collected in the glass bottle.

iron + chlorine → iron(III) chloride

Similar reactions take place with iron and bromine or iodine.

14.3 Reactions of hydrogen with halogens

The reactions of hydrogen with different halogen elements clearly show the difference in reactivity of these non-metals.

Mixtures of fluorine and hydrogen react explosively to form hydrogen fluoride:

hydrogen + fluorine → hydrogen fluoride

Chlorine and hydrogen can be mixed together without reaction providing they are kept in the dark. In the sunlight they react explosively:

hydrogen + chlorine → hydrogen chloride

Mixtures of bromine and hydrogen react together on heating to produce hydrogen bromide:

hydrogen + bromine → hydrogen bromide

Iodine and hydrogen only partially react together when they are heated:

hydrogen + iodine ⇌ hydrogen iodide

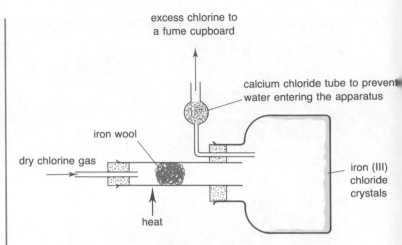

Fig. 14.1 Apparatus for carrying out the reaction of iron with dry chlorine

Fig. 14.2 All these products contain halogens

From these reactions it can be concluded that the halogens can be placed in this order:

fluorine is most reactive
chlorine
bromine
iodine is least reactive

14.4 Displacement reactions of halogens

An aqueous solution of potassium iodide is colourless. If chlorine gas is bubbled through an aqueous solution of potassium iodide, the solution turns brown:

potassium iodide + chlorine → potassium chloride + iodine

Chlorine, being more reactive than iodine, replaces the iodine. The free iodine gives the solution its colour.

Activities

Table 14.1 Some properties of the halogens

Element	Atomic number	Melting point °C	Boiling point °C	Density at room temperature and pressure
Fluorine F	9	−220	−188	1.58 g per dm^3
Chlorine Cl	17	−101	−34	2.99 g per dm^3
Bromine Br	35	−7	58	3.12 g per cm^3
Iodine I	53	114	183	4.94 g per cm^3

1 Table 14.1 gives some of the properties of the halogen elements.

(a) Which halogen
  (i) could be solidified by a mixture of ice and salt;
  (ii) has the lowest melting point;
  (iii) has the highest boiling point;
  (iv) has the greatest density at room temperature and pressure?

(b) Predict the properties of the element astatine (atomic number 85) using the information about the other halogens.

2 Fig. 14.3 shows a simple diagram of a fluorine atom. All halogen elements contain seven electrons in the outer electron shell.

(a) Draw a simple diagram to show the arrangement of electrons in a chlorine atom.

(b) A fluorine atom readily gains an electron to form a fluoride F$^-$ ion.

  (i) Draw a diagram to show the arrangement of electrons in a fluoride ion.
  (ii) Which element has the same electron arrangement as a fluoride ion?

3 A, B and C are aqueous solutions of potassium chloride, potassium bromide and potassium iodide. It is not known which solution is which.

A sample of each solution was placed in a separate test tube. A couple of drops of chlorine solution were added to each test tube. The observations made are recorded in Table 14.2.

Solution	Add chlorine water	Add bromine water
A	Orange-red solution	Pale yellow solution
B	Colourless solution	Pale yellow solution
C	Red-brown solution	Red-brown solution

Table 14.2 Results of adding chlorine water and bromine water to A, B and C

Three fresh samples of A, B and C were put into clean test tubes and a couple of drops of pale yellow bromine solution added to each test tube. The observations are given in Table 14.2. From Table 14.2, identify which solution is which.

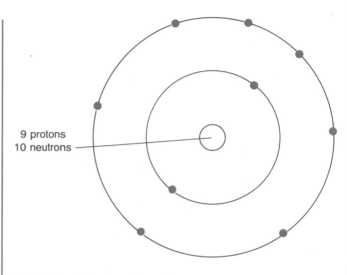

9 protons
10 neutrons

Fig. 14.3 A fluorine atom

4 There is great debate about whether fluorides should be added to water supplies. Make a list of the advantages and disadvantages of this step being taken.

Summary

Fluorine, chlorine, bromine and iodine are members of the halogen family. They are reactive non-metals which react with metals to form salts. The reactivity of the halogens decreases as the atomic number increases.

Unit 15

The noble gases

The noble gases are a family of unreactive gases placed in group 0 of the Periodic Table.

They are:

Helium He
Neon Ne
Argon Ar
Krypton Kr
Xenon Xe

Radon is also a noble gas but it is very rare and it is radioactive (see *Foundation Skills – Chemistry* Volume 1 Unit 24).

These gases were unknown when Mendeléef drew up his Periodic Table. They had to be added to the Periodic Table after their discovery.

15.1 Reactions of noble gases

It was believed until about thirty years ago that these gases did not react with any other chemical under any conditions. For this reason, the gases were called noble gases.

However, we can form a number of noble gas compounds. For example, xenon and fluorine react together to form xenon tetrafluoride. To bring this about the mixture of gases has to be passed through a heated nickel tube. Xenon tetrafluoride forms as colourless crystals when the gas is cooled.

15.2 Uses of noble gases

Helium is used for filling weather balloons and airships. It is denser than hydrogen and, therefore, does not have such a good lifting power as hydrogen. Its main advantage is it is not flammable and can be used safely without fire risks.

Nitrogen, dissolved in the blood under pressure, can cause a severe condition called diver's bends when a diver comes back to the surface. To avoid this, nitrogen is not used in a diver's breathing apparatus. A diver's breathing apparatus contains a mixture of helium and oxygen.

Neon is used to fill light tubes for advertising signs. The tubes are filled with neon at a low pressure and an electric spark is passed through the tube.

Argon and argon/nitrogen mixtures are used to fill electric light bulbs (Fig. 15.2). The tungsten filament is heated by an electric current until it glows. Oxygen must not be inside the bulb or the filament will burn out.

Krypton and xenon are used in special bulbs for lighthouses and projectors. Radon is a radioactive gas and is used in the treatment of cancers.

Fig. 15.1 Uses of the noble gases

(a) Robot 'sniffer' detecting leaks in cars – the car is filled with helium-enriched air and the 'sniffer' detects escaping helium

(b) Deep sea diver

(c) Weather balloons

(e) Neon signs at Piccadilly Circus

(d) A lighthouse

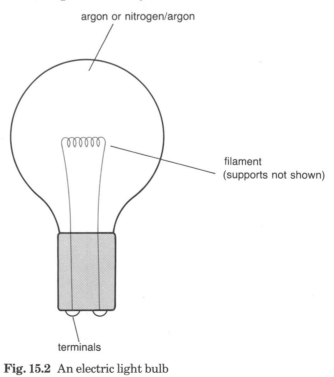

argon or nitrogen/argon

filament
(supports not shown)

terminals

Fig. 15.2 An electric light bulb

Activities

Table 15.1 Physical properties of the noble gases

Noble gas	Atomic number	Melting point °C	Boiling point °C	Density g per dm³
Helium	2	−270	−269	0.17
Neon	10	−249	−246	0.84
Argon	18	−189	−189	1.66
Krypton	36	−157	−153	3.46
Xenon	54	−112	−108	5.45

1 Table 15.1 gives some of the physical properties of the noble gases. Use this information to answer the following questions.
Which of the noble gases:

(a) contains the greatest number of protons;
(b) has the highest melting point;
(c) is most easily liquefied;
(d) are denser than air?

2 Many gases e.g. chlorine, oxygen, nitrogen and hydrogen are said to be diatomic i.e. each molecule of the gas consists of two atoms joined together.
   Noble gases are unique in existing as single atoms i.e. they are monatomic.
The diagrams A–E in Fig. 15.3 show simple representations of arrangements of particles in different gases. Which of these diagrams could represent:

(a) helium at low pressure;
(b) helium at high pressure;
(c) oxygen;
(d) oxygen and helium;
(e) oxygen and nitrogen?

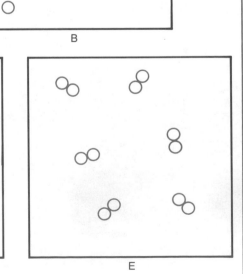

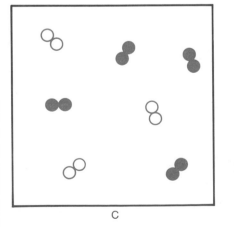

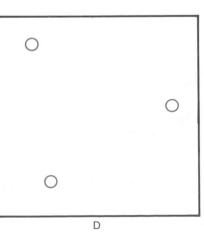

Fig. 15.3 Arrangements of particles in gases

Lord Rayleigh

William Ramsay

3 Read the following passage about the history of the discovery of noble gases and answer the questions which follow.

The discovery of the noble gases

In 1894, Lord Rayleigh was accurately measuring the densities of common gases. He produced several samples of nitrogen from different chemicals and, within the limits of experimental error, obtained a value for the density of nitrogen of 1.2505 g per dm^3 at 0° C and atmospheric pressure.

However, he also prepared samples of nitrogen from the air by removing oxygen, water vapour and carbon dioxide. The density of the nitrogen prepared in this way was always about 1.2575 g per dm^3 under the same conditions.

In order to understand this mystery, Lord Rayleigh enlisted the help of William Ramsay. Ramsay was a young Professor of Chemistry at University College London. Ramsay believed that the reason for this difference was the presence of some heavier gas in the nitrogen obtained from the air, and within a few months he had proved this to be correct.

Nitrogen is an unreactive gas but it will react with burning magnesium to form solid magnesium nitride. Magnesium was used to remove the nitrogen from a sample of impure nitrogen from the air. The resulting gas was unaffected by magnesium and produced an entirely different spectrum from nitrogen. This, together with experiments carried out by Rayleigh, confirmed the presence of a new element called argon in 1895.

A gas was obtained from heating certain uranium minerals and this was also, like argon, very inert. It was found to be identical to the element helium first discovered in spectroscopic examination of light from the sun.

Later other noble gases were obtained by careful fractional distillation of liquid air by M.W. Travers.

Ramsay's discoveries brought him international fame. In 1904 he was awarded the Nobel prize for Chemistry; in the same year Rayleigh received the Nobel prize for Physics.

(a) Which element was discovered 'on the sun' before it was discovered on the earth?

(b) Explain, including a word equation, how nitrogen can be removed from the sample obtained from the air.

(c) Using your knowledge of Chemistry, explain how you would produce a sample of nitrogen from the air by removing water vapour, carbon dioxide and oxygen.

(d) Ramsay believed that the nitrogen obtained from the air differed from pure nitrogen because it has some other, heavier gas present. Why did he think that this gas was heavier and not lighter than nitrogen?

4 Given a cylinder of xenon gas and a cylinder of fluorine gas, draw a diagram of apparatus set up to produce a sample of xenon tetrafluoride crystals.

Summary

The noble gas family includes the elements helium, neon, argon, krypton, xenon and radon.

These gases were not known when Mendeléef drew up his Periodic Table. They had to be fitted into group 0 of the Periodic Table.

The reason that they did not become known for so long, despite being present in air, was their lack of reactions. Only in the 1960s did chemists find that compounds of noble gases could be made.

Unit 16

Carbon

Carbon is an extremely important element which forms more compounds than any other element.
Carbon is a non-metallic element in group IV of the Periodic Table. The arrangement of electrons in a carbon atom is 2,4.

16.1 Allotropes of carbon

Carbon can exist in two crystalline forms, called diamond and graphite. These two forms or allotropes exist because, although they are both made up of the same carbon atoms, the atoms can be arranged in different ways.

16.2 Diamond

Diamonds were formed in the earth when carbon was subjected to tremendous pressures as the earth cooled.

The arrangement of carbon atoms in diamond is shown in Fig. 16.1. Each carbon atom is strongly joined or bonded to four other carbon atoms. A strong framework is built up called a giant structure.

Diamond is the hardest natural substance known. It is used for cutting and engraving glass. It is also used for the cutting edges of saws and drill bits.

Man-made or synthetic diamonds can be made by subjecting carbon to extremely high pressures. At present the diamonds can only be used as industrial diamonds.

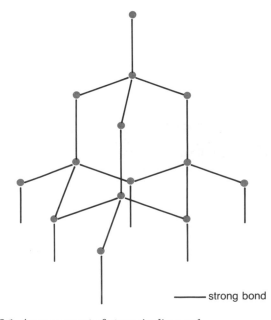
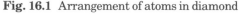

Fig. 16.1 Arrangement of atoms in diamond

16.3 Graphite

Graphite has a layer structure. Although the bonds within each layer are very strong, the forces between the layers are weak. The graphite is soft because the layers can slide over each other (see Fig. 16.2).

Graphite, unlike diamond, is a good conductor of electricity and is frequently used for electrodes in electrolysis.

Graphite is used to make pencil 'leads'. The graphite is mixed with clay and baked. The hardness of a pencil depends upon the amounts of graphite and clay used. Graphite is also used as a lubricant.

Carbon fibre is a new material which is stronger and lighter than steel. It can be used for golf clubs, tennis racquets and bicycle frames. Carbon fibre consists of graphite layers arranged along the fibre to give strength.

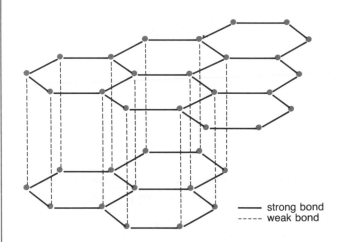

—— strong bond
----- weak bond

Fig. 16.2 Arrangement of atoms in graphite

16.4 Other forms of carbon

There are other impure forms of carbon. These include coal (Unit 23), charcoal, soot etc.

Charcoal is a particularly useful material. It is capable of removing unwanted gases from the air or unwanted dyes from solutions. Charcoal is used in kitchen cooker hoods. The unpleasant smells are removed by the charcoal. Charcoal is used to make white sugar by removing unwanted dyes from unrefined sugar solution.

16.5 Plants as factories for building carbon compounds

Green plants build up carbon compounds such as starch by a process called photosynthesis. The plant takes in carbon dioxide and, with water and in the presence of chlorophyll and sunlight, builds up carbohydrates such as glucose which is then made into starch:

carbon dioxide + water + energy → starch + oxygen

Plants, because they produce carbon compounds quickly, may be the major source of carbon compounds in the future when supplies of fossil fuels start to run out.

The carbon cycle (Fig. 16.3) shows the relationships between carbon compounds.

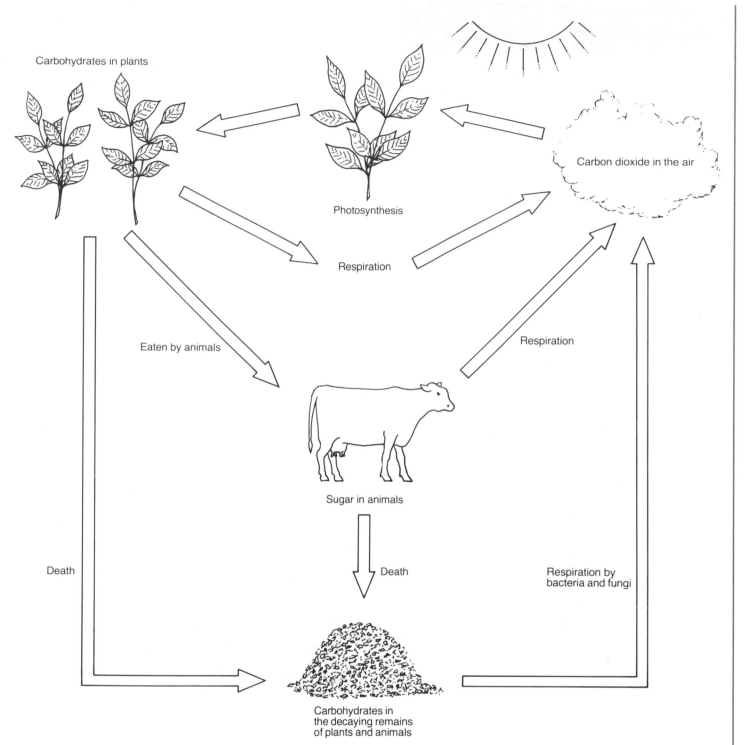

Fig. 16.3 The carbon cycle

16.6 Carbon and carbon compounds as fuels

Most carbon compounds and carbon itself burn to produce energy. Both graphite and diamond burn in a plentiful supply of oxygen or air to produce carbon dioxide. Diamond is, however, less inclined to catch alight! Carbon compounds also produce carbon dioxide if they burn in a plentiful supply of air.

Burning of carbon or a carbon compound in a limited supply of air or oxygen produces a poisonous gas called carbon monoxide.

Carbon compounds are oxidized in our bodies to produce energy and carbon dioxide. The carbon compounds come from our food. The energy produced keeps the body temperature constant and gives us the energy we need to work.

food + oxygen (from the air) → carbon dioxide + water + energy

16.7 Polymers

Polymers, sometimes called plastics, include many long chain carbon compounds such as polythene. Many of these polymers are made from petroleum (Unit 22).

Activities

1 Read the following article from *The Daily Telegraph* about diamonds and answer the questions which follow.

DIAMONDS ARE FOR EVER

THOUGH a diamond is composed of carbon, one of the commonest substances known to man, it has, like gold, some unique qualities and has been valued for different reasons since biblical times. It repels water, reflects light and is so hard that it can only be cut by a diamond itself.

But whereas gold has a quantitative price based on weight, the value of a diamond depends on the four Cs – cut, clarity, colour and carat. But only one of these, the weight or carat, is objective.

The word comes from the Greek Keration, the locust tree whose black pods dried out to such a remarkably uniform weight that they were used by Middle East traders for weighing pearls.

A carat is now standardised at 0.2 of a gram. Weight used to be the main factor in assessing the worth of a diamond. The largest stones were the rarest so value increased exponentially with size.

Today more interest is shown in the ways in which light affects the stones: their refractability, reflectivity and dispersion. Skilful cutting highlights these optical properties of diamonds and complements their weight.

The Central Selling Organisation of De Beers in London, which controls around 90 p.c. of the sales of uncut diamonds, operates a sophisticated system of grading diamonds before brokers. But if the jeweller's loupe, which magnifies a stone by 10 times, reveals an inclusion, the clarity loss will be valued differently by different experts.

Subjective calculation may also extend to colour despite the increasing use of scientific techniques.

Other factors affecting the value of diamonds include interest rates, fashion, demand and supply. The CSO tries to stabilize prices by stock piling during downtrends, and releasing more when prices rise. But Russia has 20 per cent of the world's output and may sell its polished diamonds to pay for wheat and technology imports.

But the crash of the investment diamond market in the late 1970's is not yet forgotten. Even in 1980 speculators were burning their fingers on the fiery stones by paying $62,000 for a top quality flawless diamond which might make only $14,000 per carat today.

So should diamonds be regarded as an investment? They can be. It was a common custom in London's East End of 50 years ago for Jewish couples to buy a diamond engagement ring of the highest quality that they could afford, partly because a diamond had two of the qualities of money. It served as a medium of exchange, and as a store of wealth.

These two reasons for buying diamonds could still be valid, even if there are other anonymous investments. They are better than money as a store of wealth but they earn no interest and may involve the owner in costs such as insurance and storage.

But diamonds are certainly not for any short term investor. Jewellery loses 15 per cent of its price immediately on purchase through VAT, and a High Street jeweller reckons that the price of a diamond ring might not be recouped by enhanced value for five years.

(a) What are the properties of diamond which have made it highly valued since biblical times?

(b) A very large diamond may not be as precious as a small diamond. What are the factors apart from size which affect the price of a particular diamond?

(c) The largest diamond found was the Cullinan diamond. It was found in South Africa by a child. It weighed 600 g. What was its weight in carats?

(d) Until about 1970 nearly all of the diamonds coming onto the world market came from South Africa. By selling only a limited number they were able to maintain high diamond prices. What factors caused the price of diamonds to fall?

(e) Why were the black pods from the locust tree so suitable as weights for weighing diamonds?

Fig. 16.4 Cutting and using diamonds

(a) uncut diamond

2 Read the following article from *The Sunday Times* and answer the questions which follow.

Take-off time for the super seats

AIRLINE fuel bills for a Boeing 747 jumbo jet could be cut on average by £100,000 a year by replacing their standard metal passenger seat-frames with lighter carbon-fibre units, according to Futair Aeroform, of Poole, Dorest, the firm now taking the lead in developing them. The carbon-fibre seats are 30% lighter than those they replace.

The company, which has just landed a contract to supply the British Skyship 500 and 600 airships, has just had £250,000 invested in it by the Prudential group's hi-tech venture capital arm, Prutec, plus an initial £25,000 grant from the Department of Industry.

The marketing director says final approval of the seats for airline use by the Civil Aviation Authority is imminent. "As soon as it comes, we will be taking off in a big way and supplying direct to aerospace manufacturers from Poole."

Carbon-fibre triple seat units will be priced at 29% above the £1,400 of the present metal structures, but the fuel savings they can generate are of a different order. Futair claims that an independent survey found that if the world fleet of some 8,000 aircraft were re-equipped with carbon-fibre seats, the total annual fuel saving would top £247m.

From a more practical angle, the greatest benefits will be won by the range of 30 to 50-seat commuter airlines – for which there is a growing demand – because small savings in weight bring a proportionally higher increase in the amount of fuel or the number of passengers they can carry.

The lighter seats on Boeing jumbos would allow 15 more passengers to be carried, or, with a standard load, cut the fuel consumption or increase its range. Because of the slimmer construction of the new seats, passengers also gain an extra two-and-a-half inches for underseat baggage.

Futair sees airliners as its main market, and claims that it has a two-year lead over its closest British rivals.

(b) cut diamonds

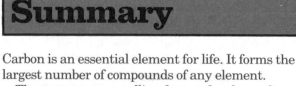

(c) a diamond cutter at work

(a) Carbon fibre is produced by the partial decomposition of a textile fibre like rayon. It is done at a temperature of about 1000 °C in an atmosphere of a noble gas. Why is it necessary to decompose the textile fibre in an atmosphere of a noble gas?
(b) What are the advantages of replacing traditional aircraft seats with seats made of carbon fibre?
(c) What is the disadvantage of a seat made of carbon fibre?

Summary

Carbon is an essential element for life. It forms the largest number of compounds of any element.

There are two crystalline forms of carbon – diamond and graphite. The differences in their properties are due to different arrangements of carbon atoms.

Burning carbon or carbon compounds in plentiful supplies of air or oxygen produces carbon dioxide. Burning of carbon or carbon compounds in a limited supply of air or oxygen produces the poisonous gas carbon monoxide.

Unit 17

Silicon

Silicon, like carbon, is a non-metallic element in group IV of the Periodic Table. In Unit 16 it was explained that carbon is the important element on which life depends. If carbon is the essential element for living things, silicon is the essential element of rocks. Apart from oxygen, silicon is the major constituent of the rocks of the earth.

17.1 Silicon in rocks

Sand, flint and quartz are common forms of silicon dioxide. Impurities in sand, especially iron oxide, give the yellow colour to sand.

Silicon and oxygen are also combined in silicates. Asbestos and mica are silicate minerals.

Fig. 17.1 Mineral quartz

17.2 Silicon

Silicon can be produced in the laboratory from silicon dioxide (see Activities).

It is produced as a brown-grey powder. The arrangement of silicon atoms in silicon is similar to the arrangement of carbon atoms in diamond (Unit 16). Silicon can be made into sticks which look metallic but they are very light and do not conduct electricity like a metal.

Pure silicon in the form of small flakes or chips is vital in the modern microelectronics industries. The slight conductivity of pure silicon is the property on which the industry depends. Silicon is called a semiconductor.

Fig. 17.2 Silicon chip

17.3 Silicones

Silicones are man-made polymers containing silicon and oxygen. They have valuable properties including water-repelling and water-resistant properties. Silicones are used in polishes to give a hard water-repellant surface.

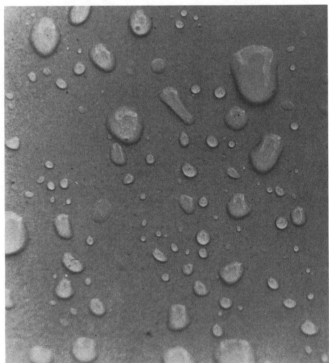

Fig. 17.3 Droplets of water on a polished car

17.4 Glass

Ordinary glass, used for windows, is made by mixing silicon dioxide (sand), sodium carbonate and calcium carbonate together and melting them.

The resulting mixture of sodium and calcium silicates is called glass.

It never truly solidifies. It behaves as a liquid in some respects.

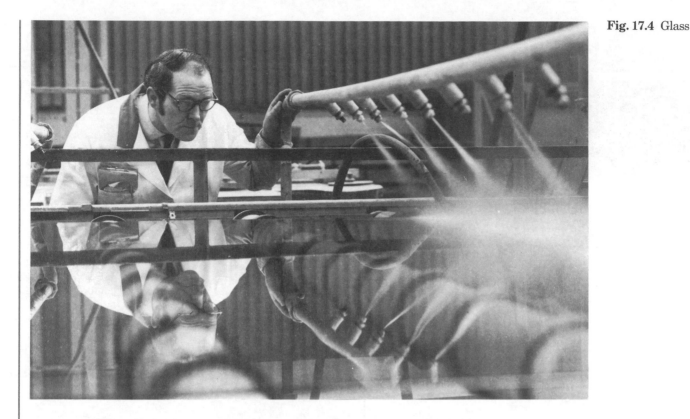

Fig. 17.4 Glass

Activities

1 The following account explains how silicon can be made from dry sand. Read the account carefully and answer the questions which follow.

A mixture of dry sand and excess dry magnesium powder was put into a test tube.

The test tube was heated (Fig. 17.5) until the mixture started to glow. The flame was removed but the glow continued to spread throughout the mixture. The test tube was left to cool to room temperature.

The contents of the test tube were tipped into a beaker containing dilute hydrochloric acid. Small flashes of light were seen due to impurities present in the product. Magnesium oxide produced in the reaction and excess magnesium powder reacted with the hydrochloric acid to produce soluble products.

The silicon produced sank to the bottom of the beaker.

(a) Write a word equation for the reaction which took place in the test tube.

(b) Why is magnesium used rather than iron?

(c) Explain the term reduction with reference to the reaction in the test tube.

(d) Why should no unreacted silicon dioxide remain in the test tube?

(e) Explain how a dry sample of silicon could be obtained at the end of the experiment.

(f) Where in the account is it indicated that the reaction taking place in the test tube is exothermic?

(g) The test tube was severely blackened during the reaction. Explain why this is so.

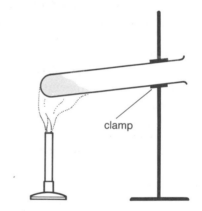

Fig. 17.5 Heating dry sand and dry magnesium powder

2 Asbestos was a very widely used material in building houses, schools and factories.

(a) What were the properties of asbestos which made it a good building material?

(b) Why do we not use asbestos now, and why, if asbestos is found in existing buildings, must it be removed with care?

3 Look at a copy of the Periodic Table (page 56). Find the other elements in group IV apart from carbon and silicon. How does the character of the elements change as you go down the group?

Summary

Silicon is an element which is present in rocks. It forms a wide range of compounds, especially with oxygen present. These compounds include oxides, silicates and silicones.

Silicon can be obtained from silicon dioxide using magnesium.

Unit 18

The transition metals

Between the two parts of the main block of the Periodic Table is a block of metals called transition metals. These metals have many properties in common.

The transition metals include:

Chromium Cr
Manganese Mn
Iron Fe
Nickel Ni
Copper Cu

18.1 Typical properties of transition metals

Table 18.1 compares the properties of manganese (Mn) – a typical transition metal and magnesium (Mg) – a metal from group II in the main block of the Periodic Table. Students frequently confuse these two metals as they have similar names.

Using Table 18.1 we can make the following comments about the properties of manganese. These are true for other transition metals.
Transition metals:

1 show typical metallic properties i.e. they are shiny, conduct electricity and produce hydrogen with dilute hydrochloric acid;
2 generally have high melting points, boiling points and densities;
3 form a wide range of compounds. For example manganese forms three different oxides;
4 form many coloured compounds.

There are other properties peculiar to transition metals. The transition metals iron, cobalt and nickel are strongly magnetic and can be used to make magnets.

Transition metals and transition metal compounds frequently act as catalysts.

18.2 Catalysis

A catalyst is a substance which alters the rate of a chemical reaction without being used up. Usually a catalyst speeds up a chemical reaction. At the end of the reaction the mass of catalyst remaining is the same as at the start of the reaction.

The most common example of catalysis in the laboratory is the decomposition of an aqueous solution of hydrogen peroxide using manganese(IV) oxide as a catalyst:

hydrogen peroxide → water + oxygen

Without the catalyst the decomposition would take weeks.

Property	Magnesium Mg	Manganese Mn
Atomic number	12	25
Melting point °C	650	1250
Boiling point °C	1110	2000
Density g per cm^3	1.7	7.4
Colour of metal	silver	silver
Reaction with water	very slow	no reaction
Reaction with dil. hydrochloric acid	steady, forming hydrogen	steady, forming hydrogen
Electrical conductivity	very good	very good
Formulae and colour of oxides	MgO white	MnO_2 black Mn_2O_3 brown MnO greyish-green
Common coloured compounds	none	potassium manganate(VII) purple potassium manganate(VI) green manganese (II) chloride pale green manganese(VI) oxide black

Table 18.1 Properties of magnesium and manganese

When manganese(IV) oxide is added to hydrogen peroxide oxygen is produced and the reaction is complete in a few minutes.

Many examples of catalysts are either transition metals or transition metal compounds. They are important in industry as they speed up industrial processes.

These include:

1 Making ammonia from nitrogen and hydrogen – catalyst iron
2 Making sulphuric acid – catalyst vanadium (V) oxide
3 Making margarine – catalyst nickel
4 Making nitric acid – catalyst platinum

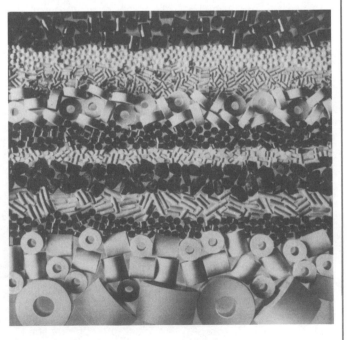

Fig. 18.1 Selection of industrial catalysts

Activities

1 A series of reactions was carried out with a metal X and dilute sulphuric acid. Hydrogen was the gas produced during the reactions.

A piece of X sheet and 5 cm³ of dilute sulphuric acid were put into test tube 1.

An equal mass of powdered X and 5 cm³ of dilute sulphuric acid were put into test tube 2.

An equal mass of X sheet and 5 cm³ of sulphuric acid were placed in test tube 3 and a few copper chippings added. (All experiments took place at room temperature).

Fig. 18.2 shows the three test tubes during the experiment. Use Fig. 18.2 to complete Table 18.2.

Test tube	Observations	Conclusions
1 2 3		

Table 18.2 Complete this table from Fig. 18.2

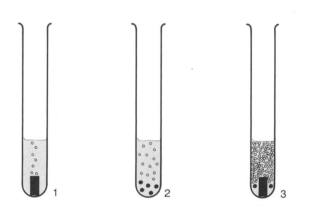

Fig. 18.2 The three test tubes during the experiments on X

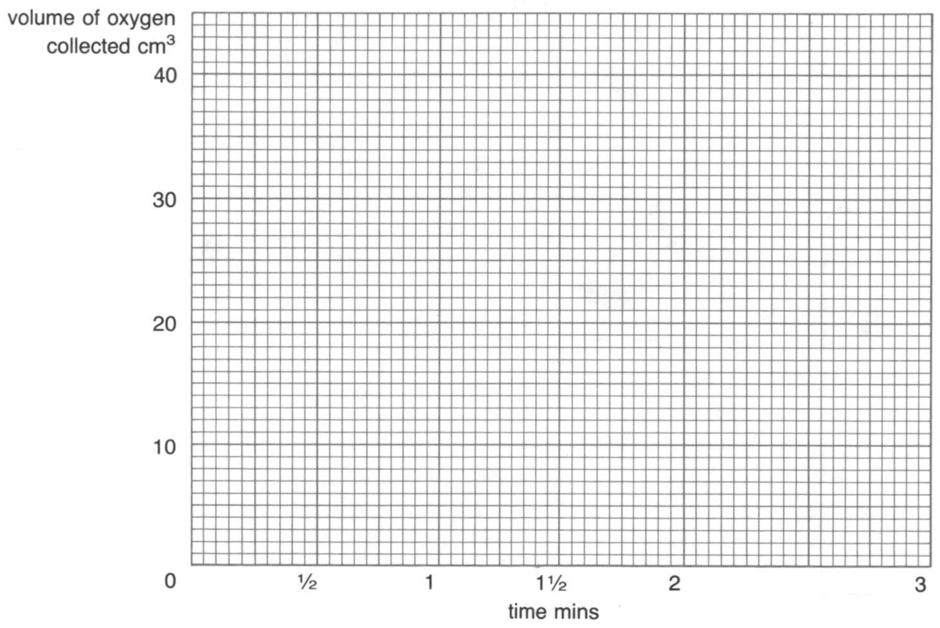

2 An experiment was carried out to find out which of three substances A, B or C was the best catalyst for the decomposition of hydrogen peroxide.

hydrogen peroxide → water + oxygen

Without a catalyst, no oxygen gas was collected in 3 minutes.

The results in Table 18.3 show the volume of oxygen in cm³ collected at ½ minute intervals if 1 g of A, B or C was added to 25 cm³ of hydrogen peroxide solution.

Time mins	0	½	1	1½	2	2½	3
Test tube A B C	0 0 0	10 0 15	17 0 23	23 0 29	27 0 34	29 0 38	31 0 40

Table 18.3 Volume of oxygen collected every half minute

(a) Draw a diagram of apparatus that could be used for this experiment.

(b) On Fig. 18.3 plot three graphs, one graph for A added, one for B and one for C.

(c) Which substance A, B or C does not catalyse the reaction?

(d) Which substance A, B or C is the best catalyst?

(e) What mass of A would remain at the end of the experiment?

Summary

Transition metals are a block of metals between the two parts of the main block of the Periodic Table.

They are typical metals in many respects but also:
1 form a wide range of compounds, many of which are coloured;
2 sometimes show magnetic properties;
3 show catalyst properties.

volume of oxygen
collected cm³

Fig. 18.3 Plot three graphs for A, B and C added

Unit 19

Chemical formulae

In Foundation Skills – Chemistry *Volume 2 Unit 3 the difficult concept of compound formation was discussed. Fig. 19.1 shows a simplified diagram of the formation of iron(II) sulphide from iron and sulphur. One iron atom combines with one sulphur atom and the resulting molecule is written as FeS.*

In Fig. 19.2 a simplified diagram is shown for the formation of aluminium iodide from aluminium and iodine. Each aluminium atom combines with three iodine atoms and the resulting compound may be written as AlI_3.

In this Unit you are going to learn how to write a chemical formulae for a large number of common compounds. This is an essential step in the writing of equations (Unit 21) and success in GCSE examinations.

Fig. 19.1 Formation of iron (II) sulphide from iron and sulphur

19.1 Chemical formulae

Each compound can be represented by a formula, e.g. FeS or AlI_3. This formula gives the proportions of the different elements in a compound.

The formulae of many compounds can be found by the use of the list of ions in Table 19.1.

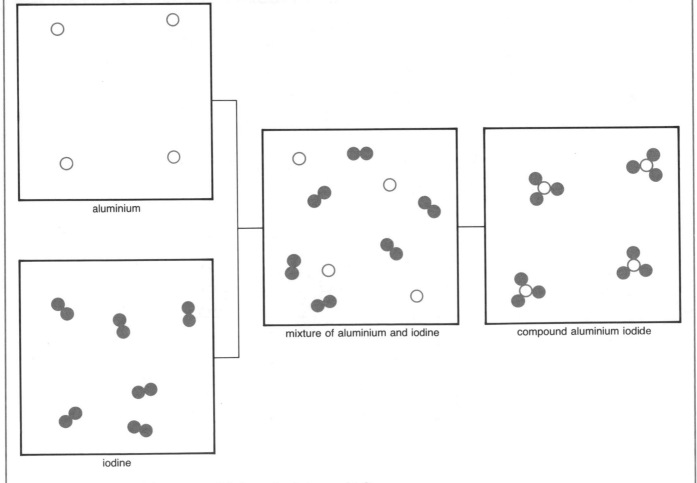

Fig. 19.2 Formation of aluminium iodide from aluminium and iodine

Positive ions		Negative ions	
Sodium	Na^+	Chloride	Cl^-
Potassium	K^+	Bromide	Br^-
Silver	Ag^+	Iodide	I^-
Copper(II)	Cu^{2+}	Hydroxide	OH^-
Lead	Pb^{2+}	Nitrate	NO_3^-
Magnesium	Mg^{2+}	Nitrite	NO_2^-
Calcium	Ca^{2+}	Hydrogencarbonate	HCO_3^-
Zinc	Zn^{2+}	Sulphate	SO_4^{2-}
Barium	Ba^{2+}	Sulphite	SO_3^{2-}
Iron(II)	Fe^{2+}	Carbonate	CO_3^{2-}
Iron(III)	Fe^{3+}	Oxide	O^{2-}
Aluminium	Al^{3+}	Sulphide	S^{2-}
Ammonium	NH_4^+	Phosphate	PO_4^{3-}
Hydrogen	H^+		

Table 19.1 List of common ions

In forming the compound the number of ions used is such that the number of positive charges equals the number of negative charges, e.g. sodium chloride is made up from Na^+ and Cl^- ions. Since a sodium ion has a single positive charge and a chloride ion has a single negative charge, the formula of sodium chloride is NaCl.

Sodium sulphate is made up from Na^+ and SO_4^{2-} ions. Twice as many sodium ions as sulphate ions are necessary in order to have equal numbers of positive and negative charges. The formula of sodium sulphate is Na_2SO_4. Table 19.2 shows further examples.

Remember

(i) Acids contain H^+ ions.

(ii) A small number after a bracket multiplies everything inside the bracket, e.g. $Mg(OH)_2$ is composed of one magnesium, two oxygen and two hydrogen atoms.

All of the compounds in Table 19.2 are composed of ions and their formulae can be written by considering constituent ions.

Compound	Ions present	Formula
Copper(II) oxide	$Cu^{2+}O^{2-}$	CuO
Ammonium chloride	$NH_4^+Cl^-$	NH_4Cl
Silver nitrate	$Ag^+NO_3^-$	$AgNO_3$
Magnesium chloride	$Mg^{2+}Cl^-$	$MgCl_2$
Magnesium hydroxide	$Mg^{2+}OH^-$	$Mg(OH)_2$
Aluminium nitrate	$Al^{3+}NO_3^-$	$Al(NO_3)_3$
Aluminium oxide	$Al^{3+}O^{2-}$	Al_2O_3
Hydrochloric acid	H^+Cl^-	HCl
Sulphuric acid	$H^+SO_4^{2-}$	H_2SO_4
Nitric acid	$H^+NO_3^-$	HNO_3

Table 19.2 Formulae of compounds

19.2 Valency

The valency of an atom is its combining power i.e. the number of bonds it normally forms.

1	2	3	4	5
H	O	Al	C	P
Cl	S	Fe	Si	
Br	Fe	N		
I		P		

Table 19.3 Table of valencies

The valencies of some common elements are given in Table 19.3. You will notice:

(i) the valency of an atom is the same as the group number of the element in the Periodic Table or this number taken away from eight.

e.g. phosphorus (group V) – valency 5 or 3.

(ii) Transition metals atoms have more than one valency.

Fig. 19.3 shows how the formulae of some common compounds can be worked out using valency.

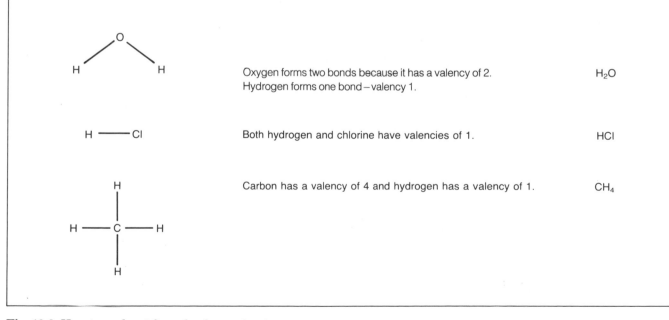

Oxygen forms two bonds because it has a valency of 2.
Hydrogen forms one bond – valency 1. — H_2O

Both hydrogen and chlorine have valencies of 1. — HCl

Carbon has a valency of 4 and hydrogen has a valency of 1. — CH_4

Fig. 19.3 How to work out formulae from valencies

Activities

1 Complete Table 19.4 giving the constituent ions and the correct formulae in each case.

Compound	Ions present	Formula
Sodium sulphate		
Sodium hydrogencarbonate		
Sodium oxide		
Sodium phosphate		
Calcium nitrate		
Calcium carbonate		
Calcium hydrogencarbonate		
Calcium phosphate		
Calcium hydroxide		
Iron (III) chloride		
Iron (II) sulphate		
Phosphoric acid		
Aluminium sulphate		
Ammonium nitrate		
Ammonium sulphate		
Barium sulphate		
Barium chloride		
Lead nitrate		
Zinc sulphide		
Potassium nitrate		
Potassium nitrite		
Sodium sulphite		
Iron (II) sulphide		

Table 19.4 Complete the table

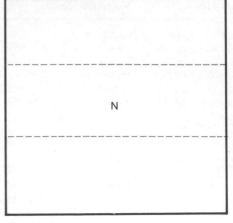
card for valency 3

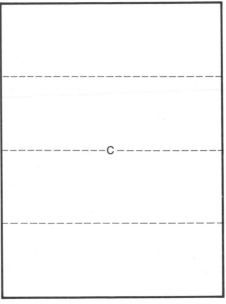
card for valency 4

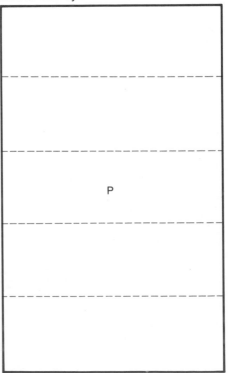
card for valency 5

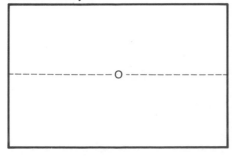
card for valency 1

card for valency 2

Fig. 19.4 Make cards like this

2 A metal M forms a sulphate with formula $M_2(SO_4)_3$. Given this information, which of the following compounds have the correct formulae?

   (i) M_2O
   (ii) $M_2(CO_3)_3$
  (iii) $M(OH)_3$
  (iv) M_2Cl_3
   (v) $M(NO_3)_3$

3 In which one of the following lists are **all** of the formulae correct?

  A $NaCl$, $NaCO_3$, $NaOH$, Na_2O
  B Ag_2NO_3, $AgCO_3$, $AgCl$, Ag_2SO_4
  C CaO, $CaCl_2$, $CaHCO_3$, $CaSO_4$
  D $Mg(NO_3)_2$, $Mg(OH)_2$, $MgCl_2$, $MgSO_4$
  E Fe_2O_3, $Fe(OH)_2$, $FeCl_2$, Fe_2SO_4

4 You can get practice writing correct formulae if you make small cards (see Fig. 19.4). The size of each card depends upon the valency of the element.

To get the correct formulae you must make the cards into a rectangle. When you have done this you will have the correct formula.

For example, the compound of hydrogen and oxygen we call water (Fig. 19.5).

There are two compounds of phosphorus and oxygen (Fig. 19.6).

Using the cards you have prepared, work out the formulae of the compounds of:

   (i) hydrogen and fluorine;
  (ii) silicon and oxygen;
  (iii) silicon and chlorine;
  (iv) nitrogen and chlorine;
   (v) sulphur and chlorine;
  (vi) phosphorus and bromine (2 compounds);
 (vii) carbon and chlorine.

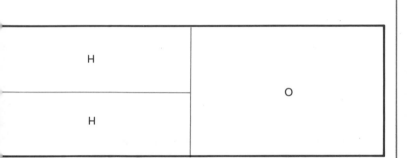

Fig. 19.5 Water

Summary

The formulae of common compounds can be worked out using lists of ions or valencies.

It is most important that you learn to write formulae quickly and accurately.

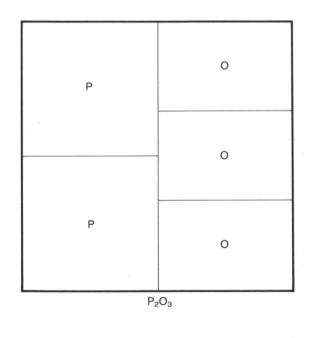

P_2O_3

Fig. 19.6 Phosphorus (III) oxide and phosphorus (V) oxide

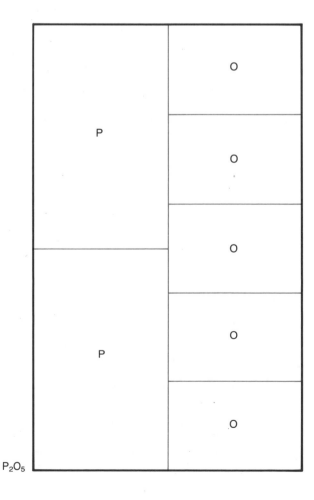

P_2O_5

Unit 20

Chemical equations

Throughout Foundation Skills – Chemistry *you will have seen summaries of chemical reactions called word equations.*

For example,

hydrogen + oxygen → water

Hydrogen and oxygen are the substances that react together in the reaction and are called the reactants. Water is produced in this reaction and is called the product.

The sign → gives the direction of the reaction. If you see the sign ⇌ it means the reaction can go forwards or backwards. The reaction is then said to be reversible.

For many purposes, chemists prefer to use shorthand symbols in their equations. The same symbols are used throughout the world and are understood by Russian and Chinese chemists even if they don't understand English!

The word equation for the reaction of copper(II) oxide with dilute sulphuric acid is:

copper (II) oxide
+sulphuric acid → copper (II) sulphate
+water

This can be represented by the equation:

$CuO(s) + H_2SO_4(aq) \rightarrow CuSO_4(aq) + H_2O(l)$

In Unit 19 you were shown how to write correct chemical formulae and these must be used in chemical equations.

After each substance in the symbol equation, a state symbol is given in brackets. This tells us whether the substance in question is:

      (i) (s) – solid;
     (ii) (l) – liquid;
    (iii) (g) – gas;
or   **(iv)** (aq) – in aqueous solution.

In this Unit you will be shown how to write chemical equations. Being able to write chemical equations is essential for success in Chemistry.

20.1 Writing chemical equations

The first step in writing an equation in symbols is to get a correct word equation. Here you will usually need some chemical knowledge.

For example, you will need to know that during the reaction of calcium carbonate with dilute hydrochloric acid, carbon dioxide and water are produced.

You could write:

calcium carbonate +
hydrochloric acid → calcium chloride + water + carbon dioxide

The correct formula for each substance is then put into the equation:

$CaCO_3 + HCl \rightarrow CaCl_2 + H_2O + CO_2$

Next, it is necessary to balance the equation, i.e. check that the number of atoms of each element is the same on the left-hand side and right-hand side of the equation.

In the equation above there are the following numbers of atoms:

Left-hand side		Right-hand side	
Ca	1	Ca	1
C	1	C	1
O	3	O	3
H	1	H	2
Cl	1	Cl	2

You cannot change the formula of any compound but you can change the amounts of the substances used.

$CaCO_3 + 2HCl \rightarrow CaCl_2 + H_2O + CO_2$

Left-hand side		Right-hand side	
Ca	1	Ca	1
C	1	C	1
O	3	O	3
H	2	H	2
Cl	2	Cl	2

The equation is now balanced and finally you put in the correct state symbols.

$CaCO_3(s) + 2HCl(aq) \rightarrow CaCl_2(aq) + H_2O(l) + CO_2(g)$

20.2 Reaction of magnesium and dilute hydrochloric acid

The word equation is:

magnesium +
dil. hydrochloric acid → magnesium chloride + hydrogen

Then the chemical equation:

$Mg + HCl \rightarrow MgCl_2 + H_2$

(A common mistake here is to put H in the equation instead of H_2. Hydrogen, oxygen, chlorine and nitrogen have two atoms in each molecule i.e. H_2, O_2, Cl_2, N_2.)

Then balance the equation:

$Mg + 2HCl \rightarrow MgCl_2 + H_2$

and add the state symbols.

$Mg(s) + 2HCl(aq) \rightarrow MgCl_2(aq) + H_2(g)$

20.3 Burning magnesium in oxygen

magnesium + oxygen → magnesium oxide

$Mg \quad + \quad O_2 \quad \rightarrow MgO$
$2Mg \quad + \quad O_2 \quad \rightarrow 2MgO$
$2Mg(s) \quad + \quad O_2(g) \quad \rightarrow 2MgO(s)$

Activities

1 Anhydrous iron(II) chloride solid $FeCl_2$ is produced when iron powder Fe is heated in a stream of dry hydrogen chloride gas HCl. Hydrogen gas H_2 is also produced.

Heating iron powder in a stream of dry chlorine gas Cl_2 produces only iron(III) chloride crystals $FeCl_3$.

(a) Write word equations for the two reactions mentioned above.

(b) Write correctly balanced symbol equations for these two reactions.

2 Copper (Cu) is produced, with carbon dioxide CO_2, when a mixture of copper(II) oxide CuO and carbon C is heated.

(a) Write a word equation for the reaction taking place.

(b) Write a correctly balanced symbol equation for this reaction.

3 Each of the following symbol equations contains one or more mistakes.

Write out each equation correctly in words and in symbols.

$$H_2O_2(aq) \rightarrow H_2O(l) + O(g)$$
$$H_2(g) + Cl_2(g) \rightarrow HCl_2(g)$$
$$2N(g) + 3H_2(g) \rightleftarrows 2NH_3(g)$$
$$2Na(s) + O_2(g) \rightarrow Na_2O(s)$$
$$Na(s) + H_2O(l) \rightarrow NaOH(aq) + H(g)$$
$$Cu(s) + O_2(g) \rightarrow CuO_2(s)$$
$$Na(s) + Cl_2(g) \rightarrow NaCl_2(s)$$
$$SO_2(g) + O(g) \rightleftarrows SO_3(g)$$

4 If you have a correct symbol equation you can use it for a number of processes.

You can use it to calculate masses of chemicals required for a reaction, and masses of products likely to be formed. This you will certainly do later in your Chemistry course.

You can also decide which type of reaction is taking place. Look up each of the following terms in the glossary at the back of this book.

Synthesis
Redox
Decomposition
Dehydration
Precipitation

For each of the following reactions, choose one of the above terms to describe the reaction taking place.

(a) $AgNO_3(aq) + HCl(aq) \rightarrow AgCl(s) + HNO_3(aq)$
(b) $S(s) + O_2(g) \rightarrow SO_2(g)$
(c) $PbO(s) + CO(g) \rightarrow Pb(s) + CO_2(g)$
(d) $2Pb(NO_3)_2(s) \rightarrow 2PbO(s) + 4NO_2(g) + O_2(g)$

Do not use any of the terms more than once.

Summary

A chemical equation is a summary in words or internationally accepted symbols of a chemical reaction which takes place.

Being able to write chemical equations is a skill which is very useful in Chemistry. It will enable you to make predictions and do calculations.

Unit 21

Salts

In Foundation Skills – Chemistry *Volume 1 Unit 16 the topic of acids and alkalis was introduced.*

In this Unit salts will be introduced. They are the products of reactions between acids and alkalis (or bases).

A salt can be simply defined as the product obtained when the hydrogen ions in an acid are replaced by metal (or ammonium NH_4^+) ions.

e.g.

$$HCl \quad H^+ \, Cl^- \rightarrow Na^+ \, Cl^- \quad NaCl$$
hydrochloric acid   **sodium chloride**

$$H_2SO_4 \quad 2H^+ \, SO_4^{2-} \rightarrow 2Na^+ \, SO_4^{2-} \quad Na_2SO_4$$
sulphuric acid   **sodium sulphate**

$$HNO_3 \quad H^+ \, NO_3^- \rightarrow Na^+ \, NO_3^- \quad NaNO_3$$
nitric acid   **sodium nitrate**

Any metal carbonate, chloride, sulphate or nitrate will be a salt.

In general, salts are solids with high melting points. Some salts crystallize containing water of crystallization e.g. copper(II) sulphate $CuSO_4.5H_2O$.

Most salts are readily soluble in water but some are insoluble or only slightly soluble (see Activities). Before choosing a method for preparing a salt it is important to know whether the salt is soluble or insoluble.

21.1 Preparation of soluble salts

There are four possible starting materials for preparing each soluble salt. They are:

    (i) the metal;
    (ii) the metal oxide;
    (iii) the metal hydroxide;
and **(iv)** the metal carbonate.

For example, soluble magnesium salts could be prepared using magnesium metal, magnesium oxide, magnesium hydroxide or magnesium carbonate. The actual starting material chosen can depend upon various things e.g. price, availability, reactivity etc.

The acid used has also to be chosen. Table 21.1 shows the acid which has to be used to prepare common salts.

Salt to be prepared	Acid used
chloride	hydrochloric acid
sulphate	sulphuric acid
nitrate	nitric acid

Table 21.1 Acids used to prepare salts

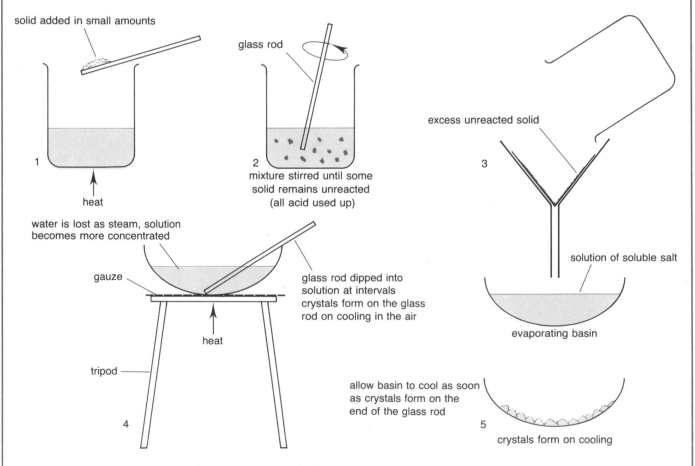

Fig. 21.1 Preparation of magnesium sulphate – a salt

The following equations summarize the four possible methods:

metal + acid → soluble salt + hydrogen
metal oxide + acid → soluble salt + water
metal hydroxide + acid → soluble salt + water
metal carbonate + acid → soluble salt + water + carbon dioxide

Magnesium sulphate is a soluble salt which can be prepared from magnesium oxide and dilute sulphuric acid.

magnesium oxide + sulphuric acid → magnesium sulphate + water

$$MgO(s) + H_2SO_4(aq) \rightarrow MgSO_4(aq) + H_2O(l)$$

Fig. 21.1 summarizes the method used for preparing magnesium sulphate crystals from magnesium oxide.

A similar series of steps is used to prepare other soluble salts.

It is possible to prepare soluble salts by reacting correct volumes of an acid and an alkali. This is called titration (see Activities).

21.2 Preparation of insoluble salts

Insoluble salts are prepared by precipitation. Two suitable aqueous solutions are mixed and the insoluble salt precipitates.

For example, barium sulphate can be prepared by mixing aqueous solutions of barium nitrate and sodium sulphate.

barium nitrate + sodium sulphate → barium sulphate + sodium nitrate

$$Ba(NO_3)_2(aq) + Na_2SO_4(aq) \rightarrow BaSO_4(s) + 2NaNO_3(aq)$$

A white precipitate of barium sulphate is formed.

Fig. 21.2 summarizes the method used for preparing a pure, dry sample of barium sulphate.

21.3 Uses of salts

The chemical sodium chloride is frequently called just common salt or salt. It is used for flavouring and preserving food. It is also a most important industrial raw material.

Other soluble salts are widely used. These include:

sodium carbonate – used for softening water
ammonium sulphate – used as fertilizer
ammonium nitrate – used as fertilizer

Insoluble salts are frequently used as pigments for paint making. The pigment gives the paint its colour.

Precipitation of insoluble salts is a method used in water purification to remove cyanides and poisonous metals from water.

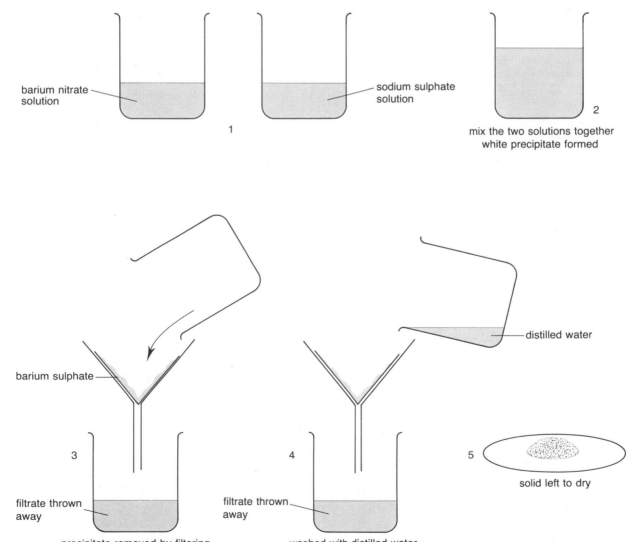

barium nitrate solution

sodium sulphate solution

1

2

mix the two solutions together
white precipitate formed

barium sulphate

distilled water

3

4

5

filtrate thrown away

filtrate thrown away

solid left to dry

precipitate removed by filtering

washed with distilled water

Fig. 21.2 Preparation of barium sulphate – an insoluble salt

Activities

1 Fig. 21.3 shows a Venn diagram. Correctly place the substances A, B and C below on this diagram.
Substance A – Substance A is a black solid metal oxide which is completely insoluble in water.
Substance B – Substance B dissolves in water to form a solution with a pH of 7. B gives a lilac coloured flame when put into a hot Bunsen burner flame.
Substance C – Substance C is a white solid which dissolves readily in water to form a solution with a pH of 13.
2 Table 21.2 shows the solubility of a large number of salts.

Metal	Chloride	Nitrate	Sulphate	Carbonate
Sodium	s	s	s	s
Calcium	s	s	ss	i
Zinc	s	s	s	i
Barium	s	s	i	i
Magnesium	s	s	s	i
Lead(II)	i	s	i	i
Potassium	s	s	s	s
Iron(II)	s	s	s	i
Ammonium	s	s	s	s
Copper(II)	s	s	s	i
Silver	i	s	ss	i
(all observations made at room temperature)				

Table 21.2 Solubility of salts

In the table, **s** means the salt is soluble in water
   i means the salt is insoluble in water
   ss means the salt is slightly soluble in water.
Use this table to answer the questions which follow.
(a) Name a soluble lead(II) salt.
(b) Which of the following pairs of aqueous solutions would form a precipitate when mixed?
  (i) sodium chloride and silver nitrate
  (ii) sodium chloride and magnesium nitrate
  (iii) copper(II) sulphate and potassium chloride
  (iv) ammonium chloride and barium nitrate
  (v) magnesium sulphate and sodium carbonate
(c) What can be concluded about the solubility of metal nitrates?
(d) Complete the following statements by putting in the names of the correct metals.
   All chlorides are soluble in water at room temperature except _____ and _____.
   All sulphates are soluble in water at room temperature except _____ and _____.
   All carbonates are insoluble in water at room temperature except _____, _____ and _____.
(e) When hot solutions of lead(II) nitrate and sodium chloride are mixed no precipitate is formed. When the solution cools a white precipitate is formed.
  (i) Name the white precipitate formed on cooling.
  (ii) Give a possible explanation for the observations made.

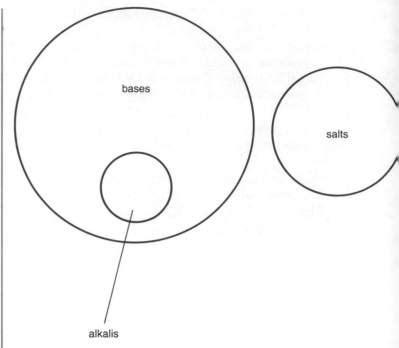

Fig. 21.3 Venn diagram

(f) If dilute solutions of calcium nitrate and sodium sulphate are mixed, no precipitate is formed. If concentrated solutions of the same two chemicals are mixed a white precipitate is formed.
  (i) Name the white precipitate formed when concentrated solutions are mixed.
(ii) Give a possible explanation for the observations made.
3 Complete the following word equations by filling in the spaces.
  (i) zinc + _____ → zinc sulphate + _____
  (ii) _____ + → calcium chloride + hydrochloric acid _____ + _____
  (iii) potassium hydroxide + → potassium nitrate + _____ _____
  (iv) lead(II) oxide + nitric acid → _____ + _____
Write correctly balanced equations for these reactions.
4 The following questions refer to the preparation of magnesium sulphate crystals $MgSO_4.7H_2O$ (Fig. 21.1).
(a) Why is the sulphuric acid heated before the magnesium oxide is added?
(b) What is done to ensure that no acid remains in the solution after filtering?
(c) How is the excess magnesium oxide removed?
(d) Why is the magnesium sulphate solution not evaporated to dryness?

5 The following account describes how a sample of sodium chloride crystals could be prepared from sodium hydroxide solution and dilute hydrochloric acid. Read the account and answer the questions which follow.
   $25.0 \ cm^3$ of sodium hydroxide solution were added to a clean flask. A couple of drops of universal indicator were added to the solution. The solution turned purple. Dilute hydrochloric acid was added until the solution in the flask turned green. The volume of acid required was $26.5 \ cm^3$.

The experiment was repeated with a fresh sample of 25.0 cm^3 of sodium hydroxide solution. 26.5 cm^3 of hydrochloric acid was added but this time no universal indicator was used.

The solution was evaporated until a small volume of solution remained. The solution was then left to cool to room temperature.

(a) Write a word equation for the reaction taking place in the flask.

(b) Write a balanced symbol equation for this reaction.

(c) Name a piece of apparatus suitable for:

  (i) measuring out 25.0 cm^3 of sodium hydroxide solution;

  (ii) adding a couple of drops of universal indicator;

  (iii) adding hydrochloric acid to the flask.

(d) What was the pH of the solution when 26.5 cm^3 of hydrochloric acid had been added to 25.0 cm^3 of sodium hydroxide solution?

(e) Draw a diagram of apparatus set up for the **slow** evaporation of the sodium chloride solution.

Summary

A salt is a product of the reaction of an acid with a base or alkali. Salts are metal carbonates, chlorides, sulphates and nitrates.

The method of preparing a salt depends upon whether the salt is soluble or insoluble.

Soluble salts are prepared by the reaction of a metal, metal oxide, metal hydroxide or metal carbonate with the appropriate acid.

Insoluble salts are prepared by mixing two suitable aqueous solutions. The salt forms as a precipitate.

Unit 22

Petroleum

Petroleum (sometimes called crude oil) has become a most important source of energy and chemicals.

When it comes from the ground it is a black treacle-like liquid. It is, in fact, a very complicated mixture of carbon compounds. It has been known in this form for thousands of years.

It was called 'pitch' and was used by the builders of ancient Babylon to make mortar to stick bricks together. Sir Walter Raleigh used it to make his wooden ships watertight. Over 100 years ago, farmers in Texas used to burn it on the surface of their land because it was escaping from the earth and they did not know what to do with it.

Only when petroleum could be refined and made into useful products did it become a vital commodity. Petroleum has become a source of income for poor Middle Eastern states, a reason for going to war and a vital factor in maintaining the economy of a country.

22.1 How petroleum was formed

Petroleum was formed in the earth millions of years ago. Then a larger area of the earth was covered with sea and the sea was full of all types of animal life. Much of this consisted of tiny sea creatures or plankton. When these creatures died they sank to the sea bed and mixed with mud. Over millions of years this layer was compressed by the rocks above and partial decomposition of the remains produced petroleum and gas together. The word petroleum means 'rock oil'.

Rocks formed in this way are called sedimentary rocks. Some of these rocks are porous, i.e. they contain tiny passages through which the liquid and gas can pass. Other sedimentary rocks do not let any substance through and are called impermeable. The petroleum and natural gas moves through porous rocks until it eventually becomes trapped between impermeable rocks in an oil trap. The petroleum and natural gas remain until the oil explorer drills a hole down to the deposits.

Petroleum and natural gas, like coal (Unit 23) are fossil fuels. They were formed in the earth millions of years ago and when they are used up they cannot be replaced. It is important that we use fossil fuels carefully so that they last for as long as possible.

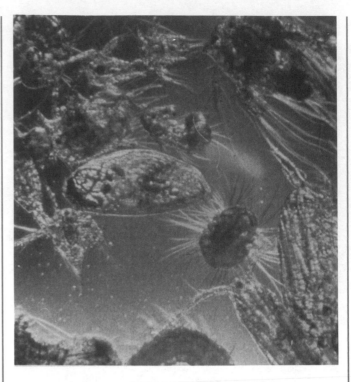

Fig. 22.1 Plankton

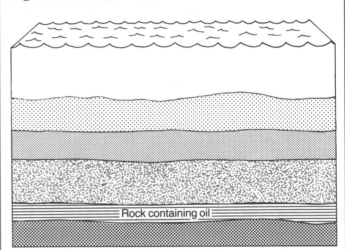

Layers of mud settled on the seabed, burying the remains of myriads of sea creatures; the mud hardened into rock.

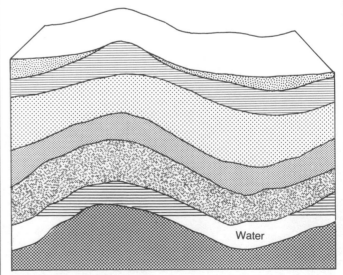

Millions of years later, the rock layers are bent; oil has been formed, and is trapped in one of the layers.

Fig. 22.2 Formation of oil

22.2 Searching for petroleum

It is expensive to drill for oil and natural gas and it is important to have good evidence about possible oil deposits before trying test drillings.

A whole series of studies can be carried out before drilling is tried. These include:

1 geological study of types of rock present;
2 seismic studies – shockwaves are sent through the rock layers and measuring instruments on the surface record the echoes from rock layers;
3 studying fossils from different rocks which give an idea of the age of rocks.

If there is a good chance of petroleum and natural gas being present below ground in a particular place test drillings will then be carried out. Only if large deposits are found will commercial drilling start.

22.3 Refining of petroleum

Petroleum is transported to an oil refinery by pipeline or oiltanker.

In the oil refinery the petroleum is converted into saleable products by a process of fractional distillation (*Foundation Skills – Chemistry* Volume 1 Unit 11).

The fractional distillation process splits up the petroleum into different fractions. Each fraction has a range of boiling points and contains all of the carbon compounds boiling within the temperature range.

The petroleum is heated in a furnace and the vapour is passed into the bottom of the fractionating column (Fig. 22.4). The hot vapours pass up the column. When each fraction reaches the tray where the temperature is just below its own boiling point it condenses and changes back into liquid. In this way

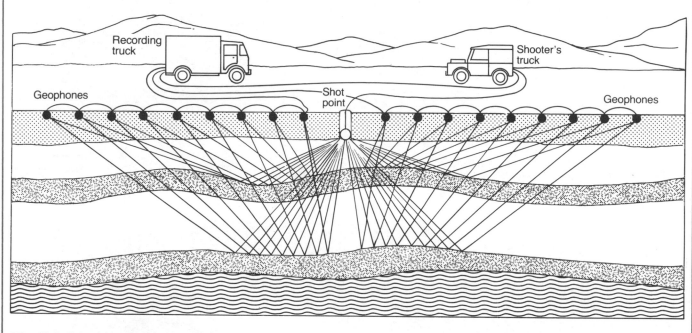

Fig. 22.3 Seismic exploration

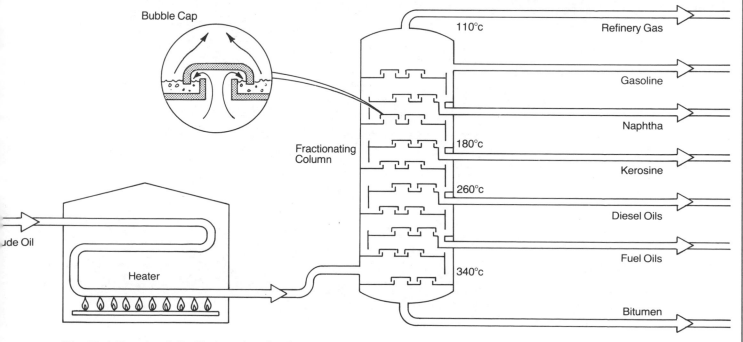

Fig. 22.4 Fractional distillation of crude oil

Fig. 22.5 An oil refinery

Fig. 22.6 Bitumen used for road surfacing

the different fractions are separated and drawn off by pipes. The process goes on continuously.

The fractions which come off from the top of the column are called light fractions and they have low boiling points. Those that condense at the bottom of the column are called heavy fractions.

The very lightest fraction, taken from the top of the column, is called refinery gas (sold to us as liquified petroleum gas LPG). Other light fractions include gasoline (used for petrol for cars) and naphtha (used in chemical industry). Kerosine is a fraction with a slightly higher boiling point range. It is less inflammable than petrol. It is used for paraffin and is also used in vast quantities as fuel for aeroplane jet engines. A heavier fraction called gas oil is used for diesel engines and central heating. From the bottom of the column comes a very thick black liquid called bitumen which is used for road making.

22.4 Cracking

Petroleum contains a mixture of a wide range of carbon compounds. The lighter fractions are easy to sell and are used in large amounts. The heavier fractions are not as easy to sell.

Fortunately, chemists have found ways of changing the chemical structure of the heavier fractions, converting them into products such as gasoline (for petrol) and ethene (for making plastics).

One such process is cracking. By this process, large molecules are broken down by heating and using a catalyst.

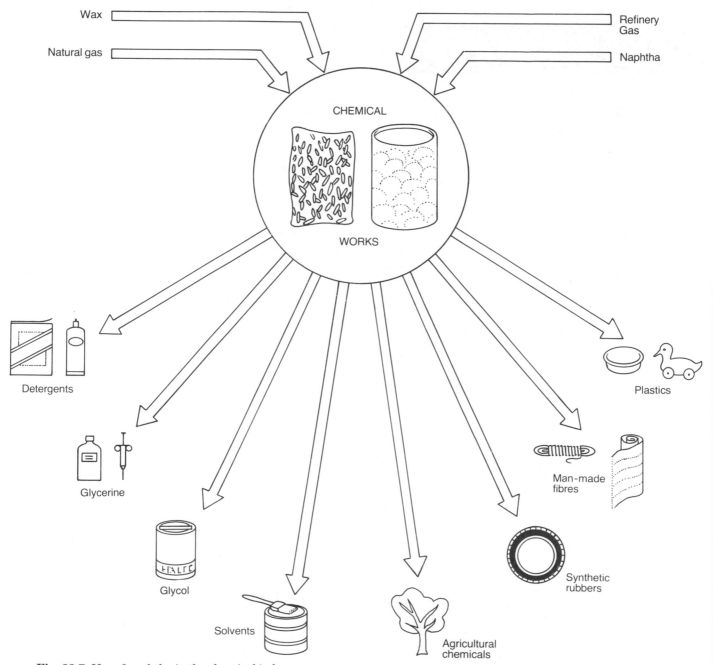

Fig. 22.7 Use of naphtha in the chemical industry

22.5 Natural gas

Natural gas is usually found with petroleum and is now used as a fuel in houses and industry. It consists almost entirely of methane CH_4. Methane is not poisonous and has no smell. A smell is put into the gas for our safety.

Gas must always be used carefully because:

1 mixtures of gas and air can be explosive;

2 burning methane in a plentiful supply of air produces carbon dioxide and water vapour, but in a limited supply of air, the poisonous carbon monoxide gas can be produced.

22.6 Naphtha as feedstock for the chemical industry

Naphtha, from oil refineries, can be used in the chemical industry for making a wide range of chemicals. Some of the important products are shown in Fig. 22.7.

Activities

1 List the factors which you would consider if you were trying to find a site for a new oil refinery.

2 Fig. 22.8 shows a graph of the percentage of crude oil which boils off at different temperatures.
Use this graph to work out the percentage of crude oil which boils off:

(i) below 70°C;
(ii) between 70 and 120°C;
(iii) between 120 and 170°C;
(iv) between 170 and 220°C;
(v) between 220 and 270°C;
(vi) between 270 and 320°C;
(vii) above 320°C.

Draw a pie diagram to represent these results. The results which are obtained vary from sample to sample.

Petroleum from the North Sea contains a larger percentage of lower boiling point compounds. Why does it sell for a higher price than petroleum from the Middle East?

3 Draw a diagram of simple apparatus which can be used in the laboratory to carry out a fractional distillation of petroleum.

4 Most of the products obtained from petroleum are highly flammable. Research by chemists is constantly trying to make these products safer.

Read the article opposite from *The Observer* and answer the questions which follow.

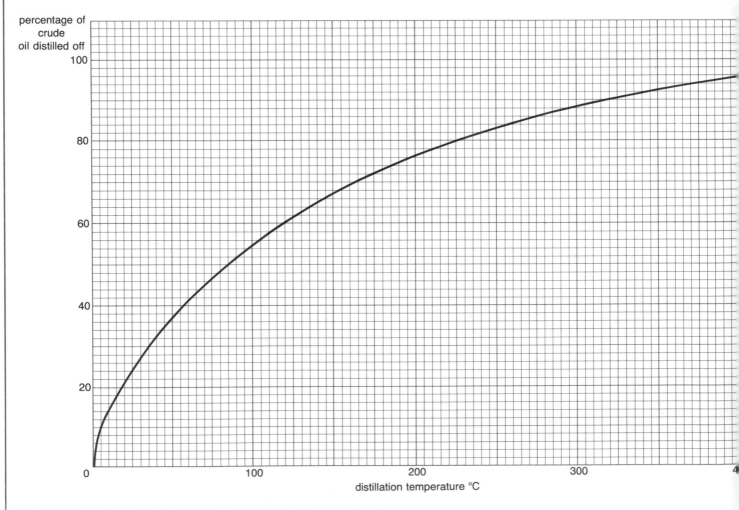

Fig. 22.8 Percentage of crude oil boiling off at different temperatures

A BOEING 720 will take off from a remote Californian air base later this year – programmed to crash.

After a flight of a few minutes, the £5 million plane will bank and then plunge into the base runway. It's part of a plan to test a special British-made fuel additive which could save hundreds of lives by preventing aviation fuel catching fire.

If all goes according to plan the plane – which will be pilotless and controlled by radio – should be completely wrecked. However, it is hoped that the additive will prevent fuel fumes forming a mist round the ruptured tanks. Such mists often ignite after crashes, causing devastating explosions.

Although many people survive the impact of an airliner crash, they are often killed when fire sweeps through the wrecked craft.

Researchers have worked for more than 10 years to develop an anti-fire additive that would stop fuel from burning, but which would still allow aircraft engines to operate normally. Scientists at ICI in Britain believe they are close to that goal.

The researchers have developed FM9, a polymer which is made up of long chains of atoms which is then mixed with aviation fuel. In a sudden impact, the atom chains lock together forming a jelly that holds in the fuel and its fumes.

'It is very effective,' said a new products manager for ICI. 'However, the additive must be removed before fuel can be pumped into the engine which still has to run on normal fuel.

To get round this problem, aircraft designers have developed a degrader which mechanically slices, or breaks up the polymer chains, as the fuel is pumped towards the engine.

As a result, the company, which has been working on its fuel additive project with the British Government and also the US Federal Aviation Administration, says it is confident it is close to developing a final version of the product. It hopes to have this in commercial use within four years.

It has already been shown that FM9 stops fuel fires and ICI plans to operate several aircraft for long periods in extreme temperature conditions to show that the fuel plus additive has no harmful effects on engines.

It is one of these test planes, the doomed Boeing 720, which will be crashed on the runway at the Edwards Air Force base, California, in July, in the most dramatic demonstration yet of the new product.

(a) Why is the additive being added to the fuel?
(b) What does FM9 contain?
(c) How does FM9 work?
(d) What must happen to the fuel when it is in a jelly form before it goes into the engine?

5 There are many alternatives being suggested to petrol and other fuels from petroleum.
These include:

(a) hydrogen made from water by electrolysis;
(b) ethanol (alcohol) made from fermentation of certain plants. This is certainly being used in Brazil to power vehicles but it does cause increased engine wear;
(c) the American chemist Professor Melvin Calvin has suggested the cultivation of the 'petrol-tree'. The sap of the gopher tree which grows well in desert areas contains about 30% hydrocarbons. Petrol made from the sap of this tree could cost less than one penny per litre;
(d) research at Manchester University has shown that a fuel can be made from household rubbish. One tonne of oil could be produced from 2 tonnes of refuse.

Look out for similar suggestions of ways of providing for our fuel needs in the future.

Activities continued

6 Liquid paraffin is a colourless liquid which can be bought at the chemist's. It is obtained from petroleum by fractional distillation. It is a liquid which is difficult to pour.

(a) What suggests that the molecules in liquid paraffin are longer than the molecules in petrol?

Liquid paraffin can be 'cracked' by passing the vapour over heated broken china. The product is a colourless gas which is insoluble in water.

(b) Complete Fig. 22.9 to show how some of this colourless gas could be collected.

7 Much petroleum is now obtained from oil wells on the mainland of Great Britain – Lincolnshire, Dorset etc.

Often there is tremendous local pressure against drilling for oil from local conservation groups. Write a letter to the secretary of a local conservation group in your capacity as Managing Director of a large oil company. Explain why drilling for oil in that particular area is necessary, the advantages it would bring and the steps your company would take to minimize the discomfort to local residents.

8 Using the apparatus in Fig. 22.10 and a small pump, design an experiment to show that carbon dioxide and water are produced when natural gas burns in a Bunsen burner.

You can use any chemicals you need.

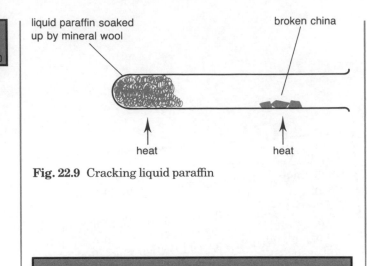

Fig. 22.9 Cracking liquid paraffin

Summary

Petroleum (or crude oil) is a complex mixture of carbon compounds. It is a fossil fuel produced by the action of heat and pressure over millions of years on sea creatures. The stocks of petroleum cannot be replaced and so it should be used with care.

Petroleum is refined by fractional distillation to produce a wide range of useful products. The higher boiling point fractions (sometimes called heavy fractions) are less useful and can be changed by catalytic cracking to produce smaller molecules which are useful in the chemical industry. One use is the manufacture of plastics.

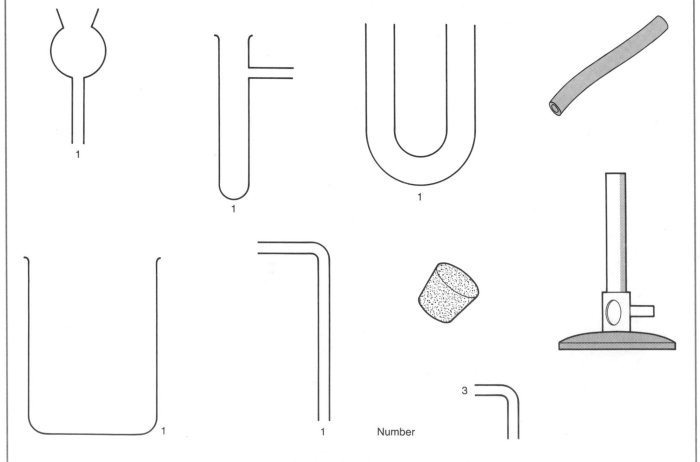

Fig. 22.10 Use this apparatus to show production of carbon dioxide and water when burning natural gas

Unit 23

Coal

Fig. 23.1 Tropical forests

Coal, like oil and natural gas, is a fossil fuel. It is an impure form of carbon (Unit 16). Like oil and natural gas, coal has a wide range of uses apart from its use as a fuel. About 2 700 million tonnes of coal are mined in the world each year.

23.1 How coal was formed

Between 200 and 300 million years ago much of the land was covered with dense tropical forests. These forests consisted mainly of mosses and huge ferns. The dead plants and trees in the forests decayed. Eventually these vegetable layers were changed by high temperatures and the weight of rocks above them and formed coal. About twenty metres of rotting vegetation eventually produced one metre of coal.

In the British Isles coal deposits are largely found in four areas – Scotland, North of England, South Wales and the Midlands.

23.2 Types of coal

There are two basic types of coal – bituminous coal, which is black and hard, is older than the softer brown coal. Most of the coal in the British Isles is bituminous coal.

All coal contains carbon, hydrogen and oxygen in varying proportions. Small amounts of nitrogen and sulphur are also present.

23.3 Mining coal

Most of the coal is mined from deep underground (Fig. 23.2). A vertical shaft goes down to the coal seams. Sometimes these seams are only a metre thick.

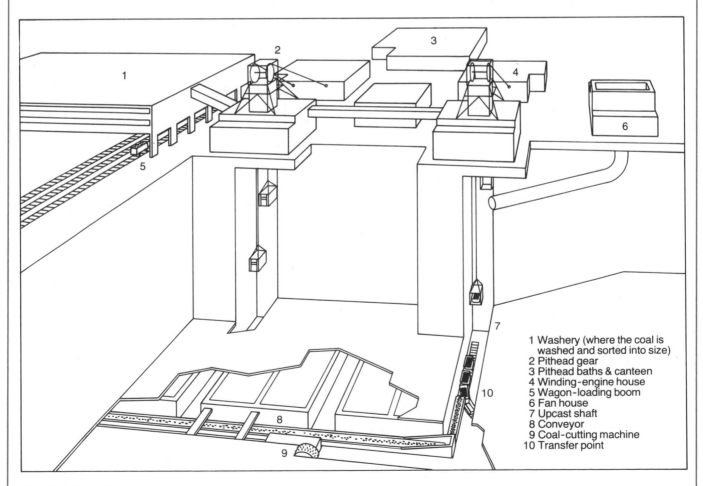

1 Washery (where the coal is washed and sorted into size)
2 Pithead gear
3 Pithead baths & canteen
4 Winding-engine house
5 Wagon-loading boom
6 Fan house
7 Upcast shaft
8 Conveyor
9 Coal-cutting machine
10 Transfer point

Fig. 23.2 A modern coal mine

98

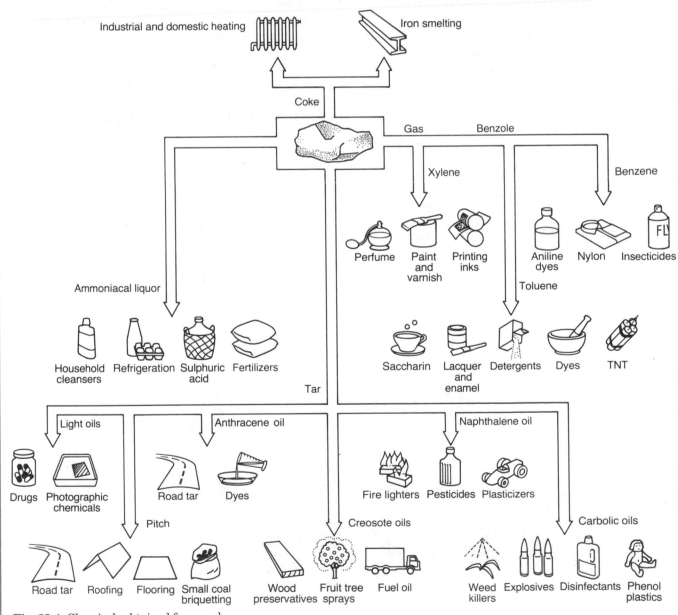

cold water

Fig. 23.3 Destructive distillation of coal

Tunnels are cut through the coal seams, usually with machines.

If the coal comes close to the surface it can be obtained by open cast mining. The earth is removed from the surface to reveal the coal seams. The coal can then be removed with large excavators. Finally the land can be landscaped.

23.4 Destructive distillation of coal

Coal burns when heated in air. When coal is heated out of contact with air it cannot burn. It splits up to form:

   coke;
   coal gas;
   coal tar;
   ammoniacal liquor.

This splitting up process is called destructive distillation of coal and can be carried out using the apparatus in Fig. 23.3.

The products of destructive distillation of coal are vital to the chemical industry.

23.5 Coal as a source of chemicals

Fig. 23.4 shows some of the common substances that can be made from coal.

Fig. 23.4 Chemicals obtained from coal

Activities

1   Many important chemical discoveries were made by accident. Read the following short article.

Mouse and catalyst

PLASTICS were discovered the night a cat chased a mouse across laboratory benches in 1890. The German chemist Adolphe Spitteler had a mouse, so he brought in his best cat. It knocked over a bottle of formaldehyde, a chemical obtained from coal. Some of it spilled on cheese baiting a mousetrap. Spitteler cleaned up the mess the next morning and found the cheese rock hard.

Curious, he mixed formaldehyde with milk. This became casein – one of the world's first plastics.

2   The chemical called ethyne was previously called acetylene. This name is still widely used.

Ethyne can be produced from coke – a product of destructive distillation of coal. Calcium oxide CaO and coke C are heated in an electric furnace and calcium carbide CaC_2 and carbon monoxide CO are produced.

Ethyne C_2H_2 is produced when water is added to calcium carbide. The other product is calcium hydroxide $Ca(OH)_2$.

(a) Give one use of ethyne (acetylene) in industry.

(b) Write word and symbol equations for the two reactions which take place when ethyne is made from coke.

(c) An exciting new material called polyacetylene has now been produced from ethyne. Read the following two articles about polyacetylene and answer the questions which follow.

Battery that lightens the load

ACETYLENE, which most of us remember as a smelly gas produced in the school lab, could be the basis of a revolution in motor-car design. Researchers at the University of Massachusetts have shown that it is practical to make ultralightweight rechargeable electric batteries based on polyacetylene. This development could make fast, long-distance electric cars a possibility. It will also be invaluable for portable electronic equipment such as TV cameras and satellite communications.

Electric cars are at present disastrously handicapped by their batteries. They use conventional lead-acid batteries, which are expensive and heavy. If an electric car is to have a decent range, it needs a lot of batteries, so that much of the power of the car's motor is wasted on moving its own power source.

The researchers believe that a battery using polyacetylene could be the answer.

Polyacetylene is produced when the molecules of acetylene are forced to join together – to polymerize – to produce a solid that looks like aluminium foil and behaves like a metal – it will, for example, conduct electricity.

Even more intriguing is the fact that sheets of polyacetylene can be used as plates – electrodes – in an electric battery. The system works like this: one plate of the battery is polyacetylene and the other is lithium – a rather rare metal – and these plates stand in a solution of lithium perchlorate dissolved in propylene carbonate that replaces the conventional acid. It has been pointed out that "the battery is virtually indestructible – it can be charged and fully discharged as often as you like." It is also very light.

The density of polyacetylene is so low that it would float on water (its density is half that of water). Lead, on the other hand, is more than thirteen times as dense as water. As lithium is a light metal, the prospect is a battery with a weight perhaps only a twentieth of that of a conventional battery. The designers of electric cars and portable electronics are, of course, fascinated.

This research shows that polyacetylene is a better material even than previous investigations had suggested: it will store a large amount of electricity and the batteries can produce powerful currents.

Four large companies are making prototype batteries using polyacetylene.

Spark in the plastic

A MISTAKE by a Korean student in Japan has led to a breakthrough in the field of conducting plastics. The student, who did not read Japanese very well, misunderstood the instructions for making polyacetylene and produced a thin film with a lustre – like metal.

The odd property of this film was drawn to the attention of a professor of the University of Pennsylvania, who found that if they were "doped" with traces of other chemicals, rather as silicon is doped in the manufacture of microchips, their electrical conductivity could be changed at will, from that of a good insulator to that of metal like mercury. The difference between one end of the range and the other is more than a million million times.

The first commercial product incorporating conducting plastics could well be on the market in a couple of years' time. It will probably come from Japan and will almost certainly be a lightweight, rechargable battery. But many other applications are in the offing: new kinds of solar cell; novel coloured displays; and sensitive detectors for particular chemicals.

In Britain half a dozen or so university groups are involved in research on conducting plastics, and a number of industrial companies, notably BP, are working with them too. But the effort is proportionately on a far smaller scale than in the United States, West Germany and Japan.

One way of doping polyacetylene is by an electrochemical reaction – the sort of process that goes on at the poles of a battery. This led to the idea of using polyacetylene to make new kinds of battery. One possibility would be a rechargable version of the tiny lithium batteries used in things like hearing aids and cameras.

Another would be an all-solid battery that could be moulded into any shape required – it could double as the case of a radio for example, or be fitted into an awkward space on a motor bike. Compared with equivalent lead acid batteries, all-plastic batteries would be extremely light.

The big disadvantage of polyacetylene is that it is chemically unstable in air. This does not matter in batteries, as they can be sealed, but it does rule out many other uses. A conducting plastic which is stable in air is polyaniline. It is not as good a conductor as polyacetylene but, like some other conducting plastics, it does go through a number of intense colour changes as it is doped.

This could lead to another use for these materials – in displays a bit like the liquid crystal displays on watches and calculators but in colour and with the additional advantage that when they were not changing they would consume no power.

Suitably doped polymers like polyacetylene can also be used to make plastic equivalents of the solar cells based on silicon and other semiconductor materials.

(i) What is the biggest difference between polyacetylene and other plastics?

(ii) What is the advantage of polyacetylene batteries over the type of lithium batteries used in hearing aids and cameras?

(iii) How many times heavier will a cube of lead be than a cube of polyacetylene of the same size?

(iv) What is the disadvantage of polyacetylene as a material? Why does this not affect its use in batteries?

3 An experiment was carried out to find the percentage of water in a sample of coal. An evaporating basin was weighed and then weighed again containing a sample of coal.

The evaporating basin was then placed in an oven at 105°C. Every five minutes the evaporating basin was removed from the oven and weighed.

The results were:

Mass of evaporating basin = 54.30 g

Mass of evaporating basin + coal before heating
= 61.25 g

Mass of evaporating basin and coal after 5 minutes
= 60.67 g

Mass of evaporating basin + coal after 10 minutes
= 60.60 g

Mass of evaporating basin + coal after 15 minutes
= 60.60 g

(i) Why was the weighing after 5 minutes heating different from the weighing after 10 and 15 minutes?

(ii) Calculate the mass of coal used in the experiment.

(iii) Calculate the total mass of water lost by the sample of coal.

(iv) Calculate the percentage of water in the sample of coal.

4 When coal burns in air it leaves an ash. Describe an experiment which could be carried out to find the percentage of ash formed when a sample of coal is burned.

Summary

Coal is an impure form of carbon. It also contains hydrogen, oxygen, nitrogen and sulphur.

It was formed by the effects of heat and temperature on rotting vegetation.

Like petroleum, coal is a fossil fuel and it must be used with care.

Burning coal can cause problems of air pollution due to sulphur dioxide produced (*Foundation Skills— Chemistry* Volume 1 Unit 24).

Coal is a vital source of chemicals.

Answers

Unit 1 Water

1 (a) Substance A will change cobalt(II) chloride paper from blue to pink. It will have a pH of 7.

(b) (i) A; (ii) C; (iii) B

2 (a) A

(b) If the tubes were being heated with a Bunsen burner, the vapour would almost certainly catch fire.

3 (a) Beaker, round bottom flask with sidearm, thermometer, Liebig condenser

(b) See Fig. A1

(c) Distillation (*Foundation Skills – Chemistry* Volume 1 Unit 10).

4 (a) (i) 27; (ii) 47; (iii) 74

(b) (i) Organic chemistry is the study of chemicals associated with living things. It is essentially the study of carbon compounds.

(ii) Synthetic means man-made.

(iii) A base is a substance which reacts with an acid to form a salt and water only. A soluble base forms an alkaline solution.

(c) Hofmann was of great influence to the development of Chemistry in the nineteenth century.

He founded the German Chemical Society.

He was the first director of the Royal College of Chemistry.

He produced about 300 articles or books on Chemistry and his fellow workers produced many more.

He was an outstanding teacher and lecturer. He obviously had an influence on many chemists during their formative years.

5 (a) X;

(b) Y

(c) Hydrogen

(d) Oxygen

(e) Hydrogen is produced more quickly.

(f) If the taps are opened, the levels in the two side tubes rise because of the higher level of liquid in the central tube.

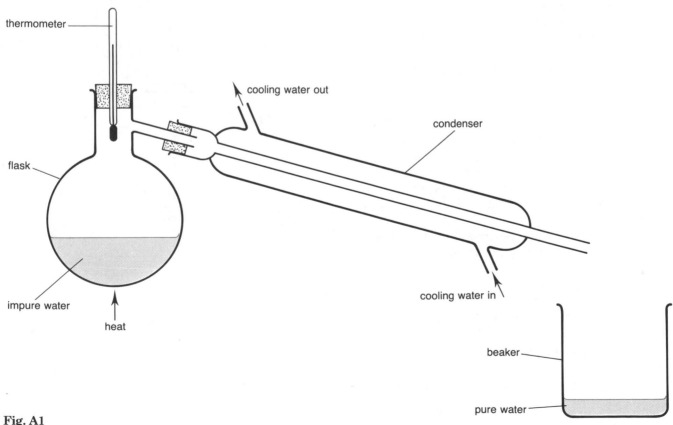

Fig. A1

Unit 2 Solubility and solubility curves

1 It is important to stir the solution continuously in the experiment to find the solubility of potassium chlorate at different temperatures in order to prevent a supersaturated solution being formed as the solution cools.

2 (a) Jill's results

Mass of solution = 137.55 − 67.55 = 70.00 g
Mass of salt   = 87.55 − 67.55 = 20.00 g
Mass of water   = 70.00 − 20.00 = 50.00 g
20 g of salt dissolved in 50 g of water

$\frac{20}{50}$ g of salt would dissolve in 1 g of water

$\frac{20}{50}$ × 100 g of salt would dissolve in 100 g of water

Solubility = 40 g per 100 g water at room temperature.

Peter's results

Mass of solution = 125.32 − 65.32 = 60.00 g
Mass of salt   = 75.32 − 65.32 = 10.00 g
Mass of water   = 60.00 − 10.00 = 50.00 g
10 g of salt dissolved in 50 g of water

$\frac{10}{50}$ g of salt would dissolve in 1 g of water

$\frac{10}{50}$ × 100 g of salt would dissolve in 100 g of water

Solubility = 20 g per 100 g of water at room temperature.
The correct answer is 36.0 g and so Jill's result is much closer.

(b) The mistakes in Peter's experiment are:
    1 The beaker is too full.
    2 There is no gauze on the tripod.
    3 The Bunsen burner is set on a yellow flame.
    4 The beaker is too close to the corner of the tripod.
    5 The tripod is too near the edge of the bench.
    See Fig. A2

Peter would need to make sure that the outside of the evaporating basin was dry before he re-weighed it.

He could have reduced the spitting by using a smaller flame and could have removed the source of heat as soon as the spitting started. Evaporation of a solution under an infra-red lamp will also minimize spitting.

(c) As the mass was still the same after re-heating, Jill could conclude that the salt was already completely dry.
Mass of solution = 145.55 − 67.55 = 78.00 g
Mass of salt   = 88.55 − 67.55 = 21.00 g
Mass of water   = 78.00 − 21.00 = 57.00 g
21 g of salt dissolved in 57.00 g of water

$\frac{21}{57}$ g of salt would dissolve in 1 g of water

$\frac{21}{57}$ × 100 g of salt would dissolve in 100 g of water

Solubility = 36.8 g per 100 g water at room temperature.

3 Apparatus: large test tube, small measuring cylinder, thermometer, balance, stand and Bunsen burner.

4 (a) **(i)** Sodium chloride has a similar solubility over the range of temperature.
    (ii) Potassium nitrate is the least soluble at 0°C.
    (iii) Potassium nitrate is the most soluble at 60°C.
(b) **(i)** The solubility of potassium nitrate at 30°C is 48 g per 100 g of water.
    (ii) The solubility of copper(II) sulphate at 30°C is 24 g per 100 g of water.
    (iii) The solubility of copper(II) sulphate at 70°C is 46 g per 100 g of water. Therefore, 23 g will dissolve in 50 g of water.
    (iv) Sodium chloride and potassium nitrate have the same solubilities at 23.5°C. This is the temperature when the two curves cross.
(c) See Fig. A3.

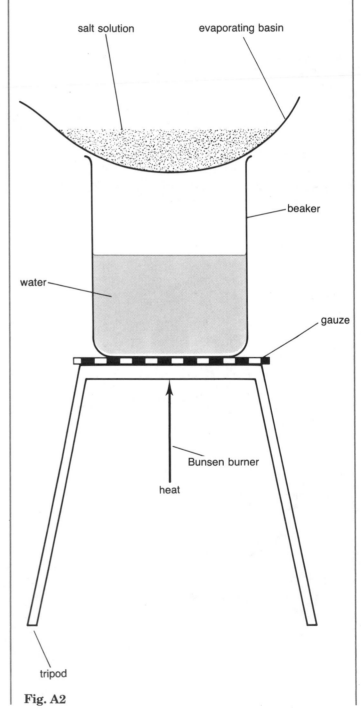

Fig. A2

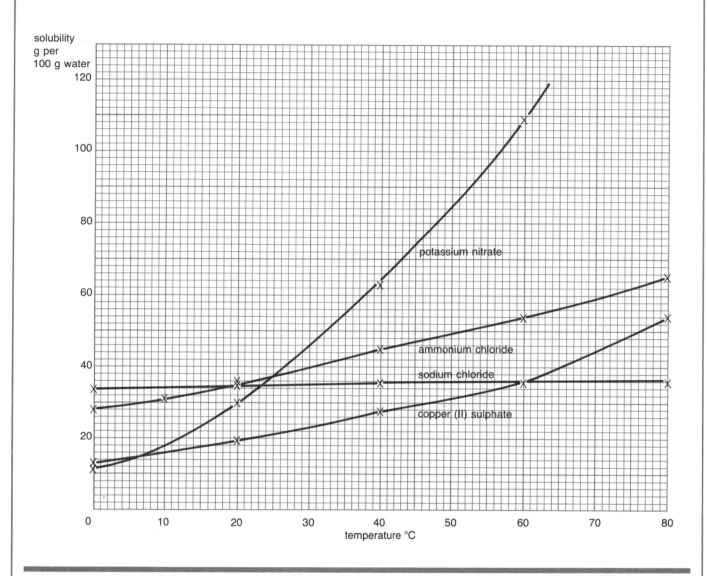

Fig. A3

Unit 3 Solubility of gases in water

1 (a) (i) True; (ii) False; (iii) False;
   (iv) False
(b) From the table, 680 000 cm^3 of ammonia dissolve
   in 1 dm^3 of water at 20°C. Therefore, 68 000 cm^3
   will dissolve in 100 cm^3 of water at 20°C.
(c) Carbon dioxide, chlorine, hydrogen chloride and
   sulphur dioxide all form acidic solutions.
2 A bottle of pop contains carbon dioxide under
pressure. When the top is removed the pressure is
released and bubbles of carbon dioxide form from
within the solution. This causes the pop to fizz up. This
shows that carbon dioxide is more soluble in water at
high pressures.

3

Temperature	Observation	Explanation
25°C	Outside of beaker misted up	Water, produced by the burning gas, condensed on the sides of the beaker.
65°C	Small bubbles of gas can be seen escaping from the water	Dissolved air is driven out of the water. The solubility decreases as the temperature rises.
100°C	Violent bubbling	Water is now boiling. Bubbles of steam escape.

Table A1

4 (a) See Fig. A4

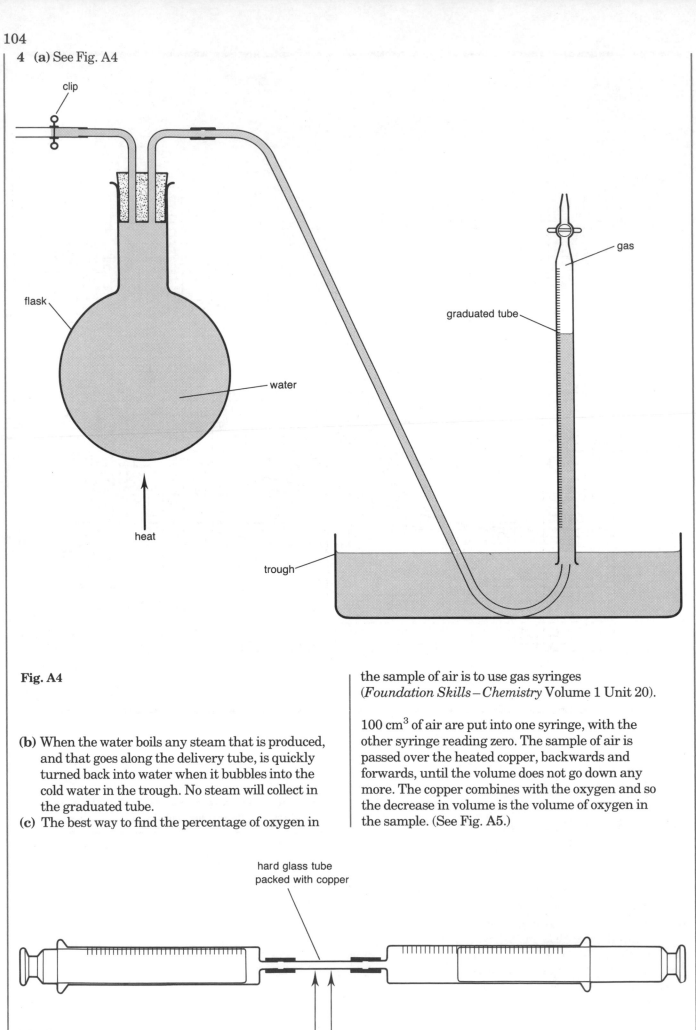

Fig. A4

(b) When the water boils any steam that is produced, and that goes along the delivery tube, is quickly turned back into water when it bubbles into the cold water in the trough. No steam will collect in the graduated tube.

(c) The best way to find the percentage of oxygen in the sample of air is to use gas syringes (*Foundation Skills – Chemistry* Volume 1 Unit 20).

$100\ cm^3$ of air are put into one syringe, with the other syringe reading zero. The sample of air is passed over the heated copper, backwards and forwards, until the volume does not go down any more. The copper combines with the oxygen and so the decrease in volume is the volume of oxygen in the sample. (See Fig. A5.)

Fig. A5

(d) See Fig. A6.

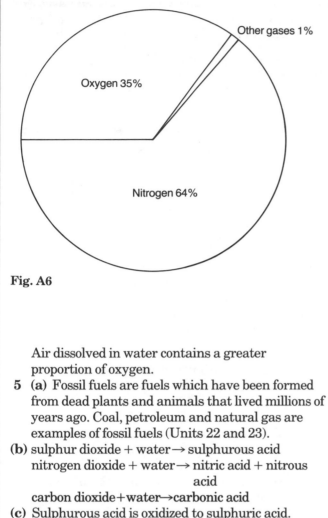

Fig. A6

Air dissolved in water contains a greater proportion of oxygen.

5 (a) Fossil fuels are fuels which have been formed from dead plants and animals that lived millions of years ago. Coal, petroleum and natural gas are examples of fossil fuels (Units 22 and 23).

(b) sulphur dioxide + water → sulphurous acid
nitrogen dioxide + water → nitric acid + nitrous acid
carbon dioxide + water → carbonic acid

(c) Sulphurous acid is oxidized to sulphuric acid.
Nitrous acid is oxidized to nitric acid

(d) (i) Pure water pH 7
(ii) Dilute hydrochloric acid pH 1
(iii) River water over Eastern Britain pH 4.2

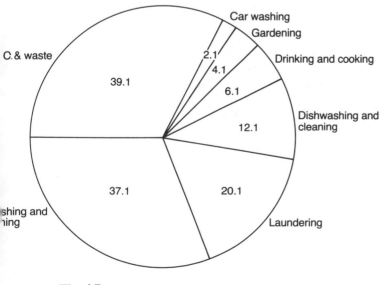

Fig. A7

(e) The advantages of building the power station on the coast are that the coal can be unloaded from ships directly at the power station and the polluting gases produced can be dispersed in the air over the sea and so do not affect anyone. Also acid rain resulting might fall over the sea rather than over the land.

Unit 4 Water supply

1 See Fig. A7.

3 (a) Savings were made by reducing the pressure in the mains, cutting the supplies to the public at certain times and voluntary reductions by industry.

(b) During a drought householders must make every effort to save water.
Hose-pipes must not be used in the garden or to wash cars. Reduce the depth of water in a bath or have a shower instead. Use the water more than once if possible e.g. put dirty washing water on the garden. Check that you have no leaking taps.

(c) Heavy rain over Birmingham or Coventry will not greatly alter the amount of water available to people there because most of their water comes from reservoirs in Wales. The lakes in the Elan Valley supply water to Birmingham.

(d) During a drought the level of the water table will fall. This will result in some springs drying up, some wells running dry and deeper boreholes having to be drilled.

Unit 5 Hard and soft water

4 (a) (i) $25 \, cm^3$ measuring cylinder **(ii)** Burette

(b) The hardest water needs the most soap to produce a lasting lather. The order of the samples is:
B Softest
A
D
C Hardest

(c) Sample B was distilled water.

(d) Sample A was unchanged by boiling and so must contain permanent hardness.
Sample D was completely softened by boiling and so must contain temporary hardness.
Sample C is partly softened by boiling and so must contain a mixture of permanent and temporary hardness.

(e) $1.0 \, cm^3$

5 The easiest way to distinguish between the sample of distilled water and a sample of temporary hard water is to add a few drops of soap solution to equal volumes of the two samples in test tubes. Shake the test tubes and notice which one lathers easiest (distilled water) and the one which forms a scum (hard water).

Another way would be to evaporate small volumes of each sample until all of the water had gone. The distilled water would leave no deposit but the temporary hard water would leave a solid deposit behind.

Water sample	Number of soap flakes needed to give lather	Number of soap flakes needed after boiling	Number of soap flakes needed after adding washing soda crystals	Number of drops of washing up liquid needed
(i)	9	1	1	1
(ii)	8	8	1	1
(iii)	6	3	1	1

Table A2

(b) The results from the right hand column show that washing up liquid is unaffected by hard water.

7(a)

Solution	Height of lather
A	2 mm
B	28 mm
C	1 mm
D	22 mm

Table A3

(b) Samples A and C are hard water. Sample C contains magnesium sulphate and A contains iron(II) sulphate. Iron(II) sulphate can also cause hardness in water.

8 (a) Equation C represents the dissolving of carbon dioxide in rain.

$$CO_2(g) + H_2O(l) \rightarrow H_2CO_3(aq)$$

(b) Equation B represents the dissolving of limestone in rain water.

$$CaCO_3(s) + H_2O(l) + CO_2(g) \rightarrow Ca(HCO_3)_2(aq)$$

(c) Equation A represents the decomposition of temporary hard water.

$$Ca(HCO_3)_2(aq) \rightarrow CaCO_3(s) + H_2O(l) + CO_2(g)$$

(d) Equation D represents the softening of permanent hardness in water.

$$CaSO_4(aq) + Na_2CO_3(aq) \rightarrow CaCO_3(s) + Na_2SO_4(aq)$$

9 The ring is caused by the scum formed when the soap reacts with the hard water. You could show that it is caused by the soap by stirring a small amount of soap in a glass of water and observing the scum or by leaving some soap in a bath full of water for a few minutes before you get in and you should see that the scum has already formed.

If you do not use soap but use a soapless detergent as contained in a bubble bath, no scum will form because soapless detergents are not affected by hard water.

Unit 6 Detergents

3 Early detergents were not easily broken down and so when they were released into rivers they formed large amounts of lather, especially at weirs. Modern detergents are biodegradable, i.e. they are broken down by bacteria before they are released into rivers.

4 (a) Synthetic detergent 38%
(b) This detergent is unlikely to produce scum in hard water areas because it does not contain any soap.
(c) Anhydrous sodium sulphate and anhydrous sodium silicate will absorb water from the air.

5 Enzymes are organic catalysts. They are present in some washing powders to break down stains caused by food, blood or other organic chemicals. These enzymes normally work best at about body temperature, i.e. 37°C. They are destroyed by boiling.

6 (a) Synthetic means man-made.
(b) Soap making was introduced into North Cheshire because of the River Mersey which allowed large ships to bring and unload fats and oils from Africa and Asia. Also there are large deposits of salt (sodium chloride) in this area. Large amounts of salt are required in making soap.
(c) The price of soap fell during the nineteenth century because of the abolition of 'Soap Tax' and also the improved transport systems meant a ready supply of fats and oils.

7 (a) The advantages of soap are that it removes grease and dirt so that the skin looks cleaner; it does away with body odour caused by sweat and grease; and it helps to cut down the risk of infection especially by people handling food.
(b) The disadvantages of soap is that it washes away the emulsion which forms a protective layer for the lower skin. The soap is alkaline and destroys the normally acid surface of the skin. It takes the skin one and a half hours to return to its normal acid level.
(c) The synthetic detergents being developed are neutral and will contain chemicals which will not destroy the body's own defence mechanism. They will still, however, remove the grease and dirt.

Unit 7 Water pollution

1 (a) (i) A; (ii) E; (iii) A; (iv) B
(b) (i) The pH of A is 7 as this is a relatively pure source of water. Sample B contains considerable amounts of free ammonia which forms an alkaline solution. The pH of sampe B is 9.
(ii) The ammonia in sample B is oxidized to nitrates by bacteria. The dissolved oxygen in the river is needed for this process. By the time the water gets to C the amount of ammonia has decreased and the amount of dissolved oxygen has increased again.

(iii) A small river joins the main river near D. This small river is bringing in ammonia, mainly from farm waste and excess fertilizer being washed off the land.

(iv) The temperature of the water at E is somewhat higher than at D because the power station will be discharging warm water into the river.

(v) Oxygen is less soluble in warmer water and so as the river travels from E to F the dissolved oxygen increases as the temperature falls again. Also a small river, possibly carrying cleaner and more oxygenated water, joins the river.

(vi) The nitrate levels increase between F and G as the river passes through farm land. Again farm waste and very soluble fertilizers are washed into the river.

2   Least polluted   Z
                      X
                      W
     Most polluted   Y

3 (a) The increased nitrate and phosphate levels in the lakes have been caused by the 'run off' of fertilizers from the fields and an increased input of water from sewage treatment plants.

(b) The increased nitrate and phosphate levels have made the lakes more productive. More algae have grown and the lakes have become less acid.

(c) The acidity of the lakes has not changed because the increased alkalinity caused especially by nitrogen compounds has been neutralized by the increased acidity of natural rain.

4 (a)(i) There is most mercury in the mud from the Mersey estuary.

(ii) There is most lead and copper in the mud from the Restronguet Creek estuary.

(iii) There is most cadmium in the mud from Restronguet Creek, Mersey and Severn and Bristol estuaries.

(b) Heavy metals can get into the mud as a result of waste from chemical factories being discharged into the rivers. The heavy metal deposits can also come from rocks in the area.

Unit 8 Crystals and water of crystallization

2 (a) The test tube should be clamped near the stoppered end i.e. as far away from the source of heat as possible.

(b) (i) The liquid starts to travel back up the delivery tube when heating is stopped. To prevent this the delivery tube should be lifted out of the test tube before heating is stopped.

(ii) This happens because the hot gas in the heated test tube starts to cool down when the heating is stopped. This causes the gas to contract, and in the case of steam, to condense. A partial vacuum forms inside the apparatus and air pressure forces water back up the delivery tube.

(c) You could show it was pure water by measuring its boiling point.

3 (a) All of the water had not been lost when weighing 1 was taken because subsequent weighings showed a further loss of mass.

(b) (i) Mass of crystals used is the mass of the crucible + contents minus the mass of the empty crucible.

Mass of crystals = 17.27 g − 14.81 g = 2.46 g

(ii) The mass of residue is the final mass of the crucible + residue minus the mass of the empty crucible.

Mass of residue = 16.01 g − 14.81 g = 1.20 g

(iii) The mass of the water of crystallization is equal to the loss of mass.

Mass of water = 2.46 g − 1.20 g = 1.26 g

(c) 2.46 g of crystals lost 1.26 g of water. Therefore, 246 g of crystals would lose 126 g of water.

4 (a) If the liquid was pure water it would have a pH of 7 and it would not be a good conductor of electricity.

(b) B.

Unit 9 The effect of the atmosphere on chemicals

1 (a) C Unchanged in mass therefore it is reasonable to assume it is unchanged in appearance

(b) B Large increase in mass

(c) D Loss of mass corresponding to loss of water

(d) A Small increase in mass

2 (a) Salt (sodium chloride) absorbs some water vapour from the air. It is hygroscopic.

(b) The rice grains are larger than the salt crystals. The salt crystals pass through the small holes but the rice grains do not.

(c) The rice grains absorb the water vapour in preference to salt. This keeps the salt dry.

(d) Put a weighed amount of dry rice grains into a salt cellar full of salt. Leave the salt cellar in a damp atmosphere for a week at least. Shake all of the salt out through the holes in the top of the salt cellar. Remove the rice grains and reweigh. There should be a slight increase in mass.
You must not add the rice grains and salt to water to separate as this would spoil the experiment.

3 (a) A fresh biscuit is crisp. On standing in the air it goes soft and loses its crispness.

(b) Weigh the biscuit before and after standing unwrapped for a few days. If your friend is right the mass should decrease and if you are right the mass should increase.

(c) Water vapour is absorbed by the biscuit from the air.

4 (a) If traces of water enter the bottle a reaction takes place which produces a large volume of hydrogen chloride gas. If the bottle has a screw cap the gas cannot escape and the pressure builds up inside the bottle. This can then explode.

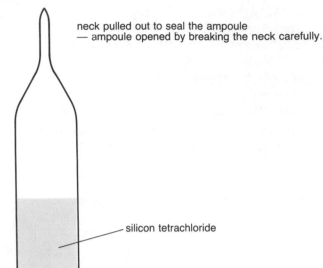

neck pulled out to seal the ampoule
— ampoule opened by breaking the neck carefully.

silicon tetrachloride

Fig. A8 An ampoule

(b) A sealed glass or plastic container called an
   ampoule (see Fig. A8). It is impossible for water to
   enter.
5 (a) Water vapour and oxygen in the bag will cause
   the crisps to lose their crispness.
(b) (i) The gas inside the bag helps to stop the crisps
   being crushed.
   (ii) The bag looks as if it contains more crisps than
   it does.
6 (a) To absorb water vapour during delivery
(b) When the silica gel has absorbed as much water as
   it can it stops working. The water can be driven off
   by heating and then the silica gel continues to
   work.
(c) Cobalt(II) chloride is blue when no water is
   present and pink when water is present. While the
   silica gel is absorbing water it is blue. When it has
   stopped absorbing water it is pink.
7 Cheaper; water does not pass through; non
poisonous. There are other possible answers.
8 (a) The volume of liquid in the beaker is much
   greater.
(b) Concentrated sulphuric acid absorbs water vapour
   from the atmosphere.
(c) Sulphuric acid is deliquescent.

Unit 10 Atoms and their structure

1

Atom	Mass number	Atomic number	Number of p	n	e
A	16	8	8	8	8
B	14	7	7	7	7
C	19	9	9	10	9
D	17	8	8	9	8
E	14	6	6	8	6

Table A4

   A and D are isotopes. They have the same number
of protons and therefore the same atomic number, but
different numbers of neutrons.

2 (i) 3 protons
   (ii) 3 electrons
   (iii) 4 neutrons
   (iv) Atomic number 3
   (v) Mass number 7
   (vi) The electrons are arranged 2 in the first shell
and 1 in the second shell.

Unit 11 Ions and electrolysis
1 See Fig. A9.

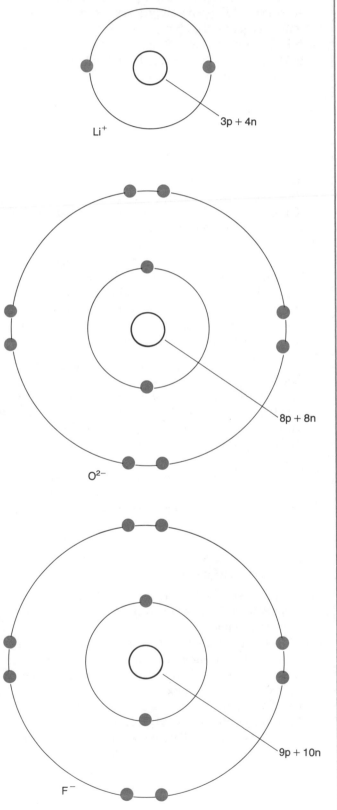

Li^+ 3p + 4n

O^{2-} 8p + 8n

F^- 9p + 10n

Fig. A9

Solution of	Ions present	Product at the		Ion discharged at the	
		cathode	anode	cathode	anode
Zinc sulphate	$Zn^{2+}, SO_4^{2-}, H^+, OH^-$	zinc	oxygen	Zn^{2+}	OH^-
Sodium hydroxide	Na^+, OH^-, H^+, OH^-	hydrogen	oxygen	H^+	OH^-
Sodium sulphate	$Na^+, SO_4^{2-}, H^+, OH^-$	hydrogen	oxygen	H^+	OH^-
Silver nitrate	Ag^+, NO_3^-, H^+, OH^-	silver	oxygen	Ag^+	OH^-
Calcium nitrate	$Ca^{2+}, NO_3^-, H^+, OH^-$	hydrogen	oxygen	H^+	OH^-
Very dilute soln. of copper(II)chloride	Cu^{2+}, Cl^-, H^+, OH^-	copper	oxygen	Cu^{2+}	OH^-
Concentrated soln. of copper(II) chloride	Cu^{2+}, Cl^-, H^+, OH^-	copper	chlorine	Cu^{2+}	Cl^-

Table A5

The anode product is different for dilute and concentrated solutions of copper(II) chloride. In a solution containing a high concentration of chloride ions, they are discharged at the anode in preference to the hydroxide ions. In a dilute solution the hydroxide ions are discharged.

3 (a) (i) During electrolysis the positive ions are attracted to the anode and the negative ions are attracted to the cathode. In this experiment you would see the yellow chromate ions being attracted towards the anode.

(ii) If the paper had been moistened with pure water the experiment would not have worked because pure water is a poor conductor of electricity. It does not contain many ions.

(b) If copper(II) chromate was used instead of potassium chromate, you would see a blue band caused by Cu^{2+} ions moving towards the cathode, and a yellow band caused by chromate ions moving towards the anode.

(c) Chromatography (*Foundation Skills – Chemistry* Volume 1 Unit 12).

Unit 12 The Periodic Table

1 (a) The work and progress made by the two men was very similar. Mendeléef's announcement was greeted with great excitement but Newland's work was not recognized.

(b) A.W. von Hofmann

(c) Modern chemists have many advantages. They are able to work full-time on their research with the benefit of grants. Chemists used to have to support themselves while doing research part-time. The equipment now saves a great deal of time and is more accurate. Finally, and probably most important, chemists are able to communicate much better through journals, visits, letters and telephone.

2 (a)

```
Li Be B C N O
Na Mg Al Si P S
Cl K Ca As Se Br
```

The elements are arranged in order of increasing atomic number.

(b)

```
Li  Be  B   C   N   O
Na  Mg  Al  Si  P   S   Cl
K   Ca          As  Se  Br
```

(c)

```
                              He
Li  Be  B   C   N   O   F   Ne
Na  Mg  Al  Si  P   S   Cl  Ar
K   Ca  Ga  Ge  As  Se  Br  Kr
```

2 (d)

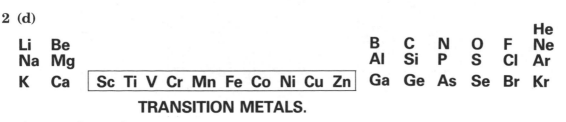

```
Li  Be                                          B   C   N   O   F   He
                                                                    Ne
Na  Mg                                          Al  Si  P   S   Cl  Ar
K   Ca  | Sc Ti V Cr Mn Fe Co Ni Cu Zn |        Ga  Ge  As  Se  Br  Kr
              TRANSITION METALS.
```

Argon and potassium

(e) The following are generalizations and you will find exceptions.

(i) Across each period or row each element contains one electron more than the element before it. This electron goes in the outer shell except in the case of transition metals.
Down each group or column you will notice that the elements have the same number of electrons in the outer shell. For example, all elements in group II have two electrons in the outer shell. The similarity in outer shell electron arrangements cause similar chemical properties.

(ii) In each period the melting point rises and then falls. In each group the melting point increases down the group.

(iii) In each period the boiling point rises and then falls. In each group the boiling point increases down the group.

3 (i) Na and F; (ii) F and Br; (iii) Na; (iv) Br; (v) Ni; (vi) He; (vii) Na; (viii) Br; (ix) F; (x) He

Unit 13 The alkali metals

1 The top is off the bottle of potassium. He is not wearing goggles and he should also use a safety screen. There is a lump of potassium on the bench. There is a pool of water on the bench. The Bunsen burner is too near the edge of the bench.

2 (a) (i) lithium; (ii) caesium; (iii) potassium; (iv) caesium; (v) sodium; (vi) lithium

(b) The results can vary depending upon how you draw your graph. In the graph shown (Fig. A10) the value for the boiling point of francium would be 580°C.

(c) (i) 21°C; (ii) 2.3 g per cm^3; (iii) FrCl; (iv) Fr$_2$O

3 (a) Davy discovered potassium, sodium, barium and strontium

(b) Faraday

Unit 14 The halogens

1 (a) (i) bromine; (ii) fluorine; (iii) iodine; (iv) iodine.

(b) Astatine would be a solid at room temperature and pressure having a melting point of about 200°C and a boiling point of over 300°C. The density of astatine should be about 7 g per cm^3.

2 (a) See Fig. A11.

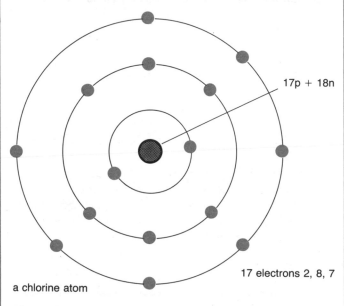

17p + 18n

17 electrons 2, 8, 7

a chlorine atom

Fig. A11

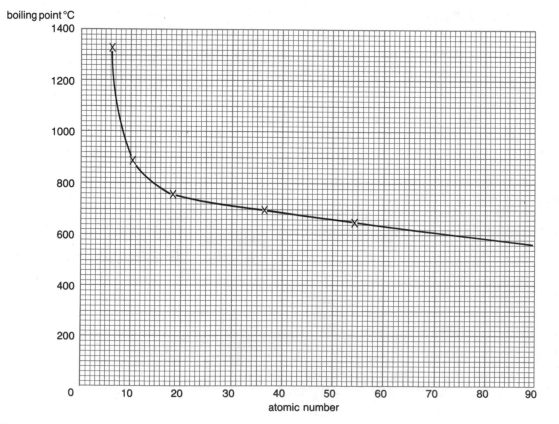

boiling point °C

atomic number

Fig. A10

(b) (i) See Fig. A12.

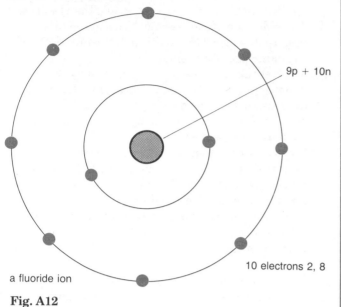

a fluoride ion

Fig. A12

(ii) Neon has 10 electrons arranged 2,8.

3 Solution A reacts with chlorine but not with bromine.

Solution B does not react with either chlorine or bromine.

Solution C reacts with chlorine and bromine.

Solution A must be potassium bromide solution.

Solution B must be potassium chloride solution.

Solution C must be potassium iodide solution.

4 Fluorides added to water reduce the amount of tooth decay. By adding fluorides to tap water the teeth of the population should improve.

Some people, however, are concerned about the effects that fluoride might have on our bodies.

In some areas fluorides are naturally present in water and there is less tooth decay and no certain evidence of other problems caused by fluorides.

No other chemical is added to tap water to make us healthier. Some people think we should be able to choose whether we want fluoride in our drinking water.

Unit 15 The noble gases

1 (a) xenon; **(b)** xenon; **(c)** xenon.

(d) The density of air is about 1.25 g per dm^3 and so argon, krypton and xenon are denser than air.

2 (a) D; **(b)** B; **(c)** E; **(d)** A; **(e)** C

3 (a) Helium was discovered 'on the sun'.

(b) Nitrogen can be removed from the sample of 'nitrogen' obtained from the air by passing the gas over heated magnesium, which will react with the nitrogen.

magnesium + nitrogen → magnesium nitride

(c) The carbon dioxide could be removed by bubbling the gas through an aqueous solution of potassium hydroxide or sodium hydroxide. The gas could be dried by bubbling it through concentrated sulphuric acid and the oxygen removed by passing the gas over heated coppper turnings. This would leave a sample of nitrogen containing a small amount of the noble gases.

(d) The gases mixed with the nitrogen were heavier because they had a density slightly higher than pure nitrogen. 1.2575 g per dm^3 compared with 1.2505 g per cm^3.

4 See Fig. A13.

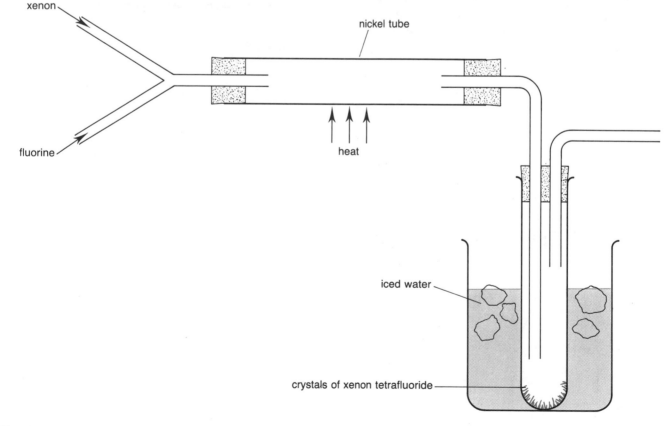

Fig. A13

Unit 16 Carbon

1 (a) Diamond has been highly valued for thousands of years mainly because of its hardness and reflection and refraction of light.

(b) Apart from its size, the price is affected by the way it is cut, its clarity and its colour.

(c) One carat = 0.2 g. A diamond weighing 600 g will have a weight of 3 000 carats.

(d) The price of diamonds fell because more diamonds were released onto the market. This was mainly caused by Russians using diamonds to pay for wheat and other imports.

(e) The black pods from the locust tree all have very similar mass when they dry out. They were used in the Middle East to weigh pearls.

2 (a) The fibres must be heated in an atmosphere of a noble gas to prevent the carbon burning..
At 1 000°C in ordinary air the carbon would burn and form carbon dioxide.

(b) The advantages of making the seats from carbon fibre are that they are lighter and smaller. This means that the plane will be able to save fuel or carry more passengers.

(c) The disadvantages of the carbon fibre seats is that they are 29 per cent more expensive than the present metal ones.

Unit 17 Silicon

1 (a) silicon dioxide + magnesium → magnesium oxide + silicon

(b) Magnesium is used rather than iron because it is more reactive. Iron is not reactive enough to remove the oxygen from the silicon.

(c) Reduction is the removal of oxygen. See glossary.

(d) There should be no unreacted silicon dioxide because an excess (i.e. more than enough) of magnesium was used.

(e) The mixture should be filtered and the residue washed with water. The solid should then be dried.

(f) The reduction is exothermic. You can tell this because the glow spread through the mixture after the flame had been removed.

(g) The test tube becomes blackened because the magnesium reacts with the silicates in the glass.

2 (a) Asbestos has been widely used in buildings because it will not burn and because it has good insulating properties.

(b) It has now been found that certain types of asbestos can cause serious illness including cancer. Fibres, especially from blue asbestos, can escape into the air and enter the lungs.

Substitutes made from clay or ceramic materials are now used. If any asbestos is found in a building it should be removed only with the greatest care by experts.

3 The other elements in group IV are germanium, tin and lead. The elements become more metallic down the group.

Unit 18 The transition metals

1

Test tube	Observations	Conclusions
5cm^3 acid + X sheet	Steady stream of bubbles	X sheet reacts slowly
5cm^3 acid + X powder	Faster stream of bubbles	X powder reacts faster than the sheet
5cm^3 acid + X sheet + copper	Very fast stream of bubbles	Faster reaction. The copper speeds up the reaction.

Table A6

2 (a) See Fig. A14.

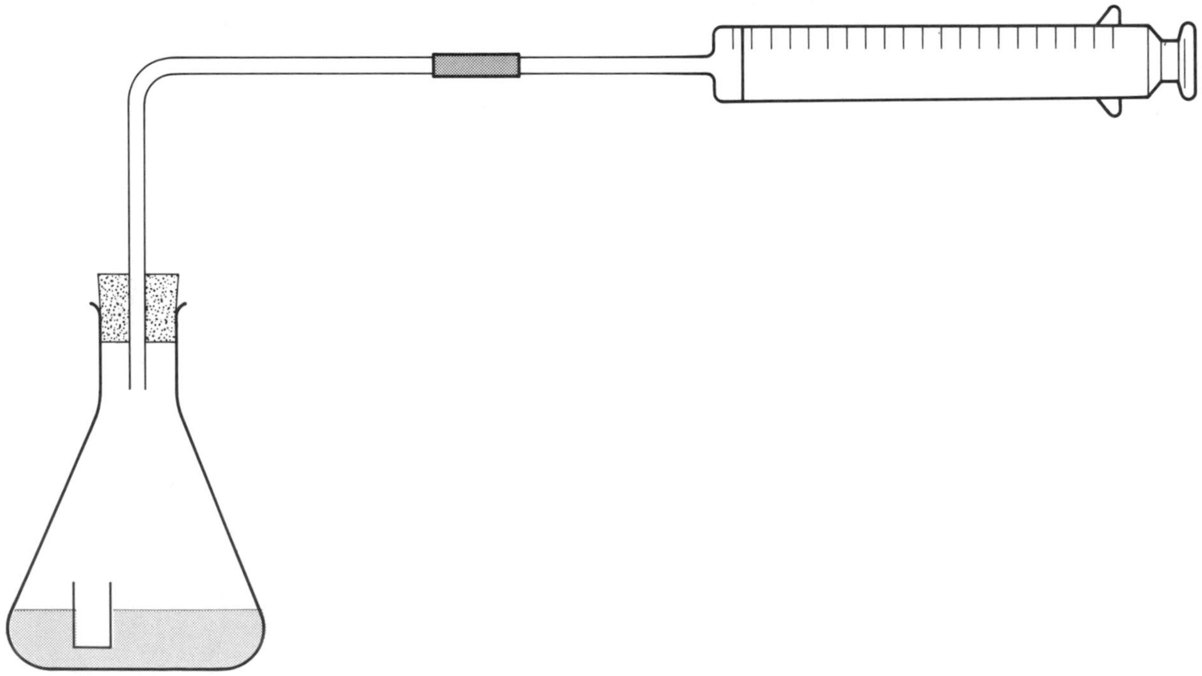

Fig. A14

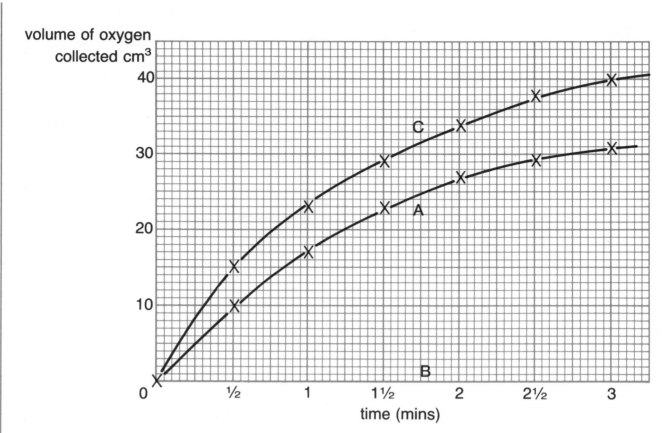

Fig. A15

(b) See Fig. A15.
(c) Substance B does not catalyse the reaction.
(d) Substance C is the best catalyst.
(e) 1 g of A would remain because a catalyst is not used up.

Unit 19   Chemical formulae

1

Compound	Ions present	Formula
Sodium sulphate	Na^+ SO_4^{2-}	Na_2SO_4
Sodium hydrogencarbonate	Na^+ HCO_3^-	$NaHCO_3$
Sodium oxide	Na^+ O^{2-}	Na_2O
Sodium phosphate	Na^+ PO_4^{3-}	Na_3PO_4
Calcium nitrate	Ca^{2+} NO_3^-	$Ca(NO_3)_2$
Calcium carbonate	Ca^{2+} CO_3^{2-}	$CaCO_3$
Calcium hydrogencarbonate	Ca^{2+} HCO_3^-	$Ca(HCO_3)_2$
Calcium phosphate	Ca^{2+} PO_4^{3-}	$Ca_3(PO_4)_2$
Calcium hydroxide	Ca^{2+} OH^-	$Ca(OH)_2$
Iron (III) chloride	Fe^{3+} Cl^-	$FeCl_3$
Iron (II) sulphate	Fe^{2+} SO_4^{2-}	$FeSO_4$
Phosphoric acid	H^+ PO_4^{3-}	H_3PO_4
Aluminium sulphate	Al^{3+} SO_4^{2-}	$Al_2(SO_4)_3$
Ammonium nitrate	NH_4^+ NO_3^-	NH_4NO_3
Ammonium sulphate	NH_4^+ SO_4^{2-}	$(NH_4)_2SO_4$
Barium sulphate	Ba^{2+} SO_4^{2-}	$BaSO_4$
Barium chloride	Ba^{2+} Cl^-	$BaCl_2$
Lead nitrate	Pb^{2+} NO_3^-	$Pb(NO_3)_2$
Zinc sulphide	Zn^{2+} S^{2-}	ZnS
Potassium nitrate	K^+ NO_3^-	KNO_3
Potassium nitrite	K^+ NO_2^-	KNO_2
Sodium sulphite	Na^+ SO_3^{2-}	Na_2SO_3
Iron (II) sulphide	Fe^{2+} S^{2-}	FeS

Table A7

2 (ii), (iii), (v)
3 D
4 (i) HF; (ii) SiO_2; (iii) $SiCl_4$; (iv) NCl_3;
   (v) SCl_2; (vi) PBr_3, PBr_5; (vii) CCl_4

Unit 20   Chemical equations

1 (a) iron + hydrogen chloride → iron (II) chloride + hydrogen
   iron + chlorine → iron (III) chloride
(b) $Fe(s) + 2HCl(g) \rightarrow FeCl_2(s) + H_2(g)$
   $2Fe(s) + 3Cl_2(g) \rightarrow 2FeCl_3(s)$
2 (a) copper(II) oxide + carbon → copper + carbon dioxide
(b) $2CuO(s) + C(s) \rightarrow 2Cu(s) + CO_2(g)$
3 hydrogen peroxide → water + oxygen
   $2H_2O_2(aq) \rightarrow 2H_2O(l) + O_2(g)$
   hydrogen + chlorine → hydrogen chloride
   $H_2(g) + Cl_2(g) \rightarrow 2HCl(g)$
   nitrogen + hydrogen ⇌ ammonia
   $N_2(g) + 3H_2(g) \rightleftharpoons 2NH_3(g)$
   sodium + oxygen → sodium oxide
   $4Na(s) + O_2(g) \rightarrow 2Na_2O(s)$
   sodium + water → sodium hydroxide + hydrogen
   $2Na(s) + 2H_2O(l) \rightarrow 2NaOH(aq) + H_2(g)$
   copper + oxygen → copper(II) oxide
   $2Cu(s) + O_2(g) \rightarrow 2CuO(s)$
   sodium + chlorine → sodium chloride
   $2Na(s) + Cl_2(g) \rightarrow 2NaCl(s)$
   sulphur dioxide + oxygen ⇌ sulphur trioxide
   $2SO_2(g) + O_2(g) \rightleftharpoons 2SO_3(g)$
4 (a) Precipitation; (b) Synthesis; (c) Redox;
   (d) Decomposition

Unit 21 Salts

1 See Fig. A16.

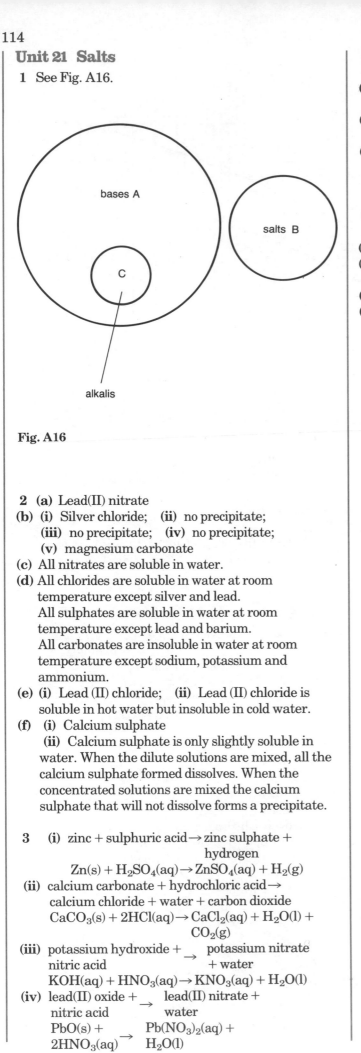

Fig. A16

2 (a) Lead(II) nitrate
(b) (i) Silver chloride;   (ii) no precipitate;
      (iii) no precipitate;   (iv) no precipitate;
      (v) magnesium carbonate
(c) All nitrates are soluble in water.
(d) All chlorides are soluble in water at room
     temperature except silver and lead.
     All sulphates are soluble in water at room
     temperature except lead and barium.
     All carbonates are insoluble in water at room
     temperature except sodium, potassium and
     ammonium.
(e) (i) Lead (II) chloride;   (ii) Lead (II) chloride is
     soluble in hot water but insoluble in cold water.
(f) (i) Calcium sulphate
     (ii) Calcium sulphate is only slightly soluble in
     water. When the dilute solutions are mixed, all the
     calcium sulphate formed dissolves. When the
     concentrated solutions are mixed the calcium
     sulphate that will not dissolve forms a precipitate.

3 (i) zinc + sulphuric acid→zinc sulphate +
                              hydrogen
       $Zn(s) + H_2SO_4(aq) \rightarrow ZnSO_4(aq) + H_2(g)$
(ii) calcium carbonate + hydrochloric acid→
      calcium chloride + water + carbon dioxide
      $CaCO_3(s) + 2HCl(aq) \rightarrow CaCl_2(aq) + H_2O(l) +$
                              $CO_2(g)$
(iii) potassium hydroxide + $\rightarrow$ potassium nitrate
       nitric acid   + water
       $KOH(aq) + HNO_3(aq) \rightarrow KNO_3(aq) + H_2O(l)$
(iv) lead(II) oxide + $\rightarrow$ lead(II) nitrate +
      nitric acid   water
      $PbO(s) + $ $\rightarrow$ $Pb(NO_3)_2(aq) +$
      $2HNO_3(aq)$ $H_2O(l)$

4 (a) The magnesium oxide reacts much faster with
        hot acid.
(b) Excess magnesium oxide is added to make sure
     that all the acid is used up.
(c) The excess magnesium oxide is removed by
     filtering the mixture.
(d) The magnesium sulphate is not evaporated to
     dryness as this would drive off the water of
     crystallization and leave anhydrous magnesium
     sulphate.

5 (a) Sodium hydroxide + $\rightarrow$ sodium chloride +
        hydrochloric acid   water
(b) $NaOH(aq) + HCl(aq) \rightarrow NaCl(aq) + H_2O(l)$
(c) (i) a pipette;   (ii) a dropping pipette;
     (iii) a burette
(d) The pH is 7. The solution is neutral.
(e) See Fig. A17.

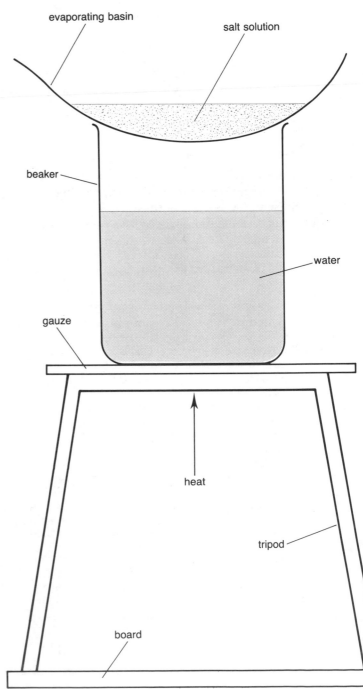

Fig. A17

Unit 22 Petroleum

1 Factors considered when siting a new oil refinery; on the coast with a deep water channel so that large oil-tankers can unload. Large area of cheap land away from a town or city, in case of accident, but close enough to ensure a supply of labour. Close to chemical works to use products of the refining. Good links with other users, e.g. airports.

2

Fraction	Percentage	Approx. angle for pie chart
Below 70°C	45%	160°
70°–120°	15%	54°
120°–170°	11%	40°
170°–220°	8%	29°
220°–270°	6%	21°
270°–320°	5%	18°
Over 320°	10%	36°

Table A8

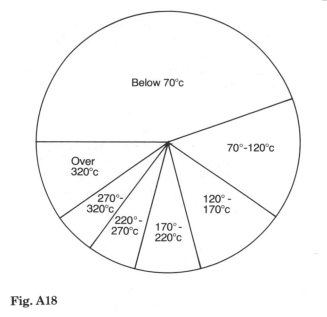

Fig. A18

See Fig. A18

The smaller molecules, i.e. those in the lower boiling point fractions, are more useful as fuels and for making plastics. This means that samples of crude oil containing a greater amount of the lower boiling point fractions will be more expensive.

3 See Fig. A19.

4 (a) The additive is added to the fuel to try and prevent a fire mist of fuel forming round the broken fuel tanks in a crash. It is this mist which easily ignites.

(b) FM9 is a polymer. It is made up of long chains of carbon atoms.

(c) On sudden impact the chains of atoms link together and cause the fuel and polymer to form a jelly. This prevents the fuel leaking and forming the dangerous mist.

(d) Before the fuel in jelly form goes into the engine, the long polymer chains must be broken. This is done by a mechanical 'slicer' which 'chops up' the chains.

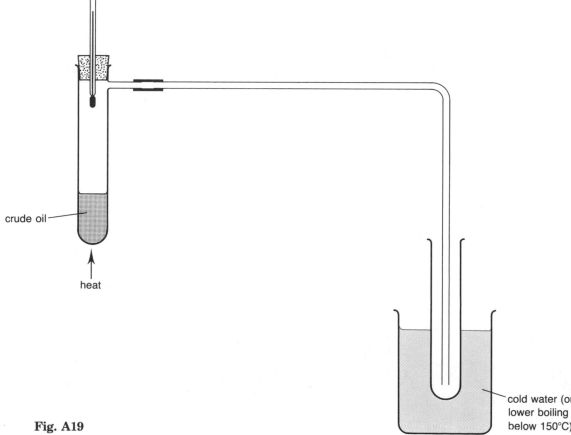

Fig. A19

6 (a) The fact that the liquid paraffin is difficult to pour suggests that it contains fairly long chain molecules, certainly much longer than the molecules in petrol. The runniness of the liquid is called its viscosity.

(b) See Fig. A20.

8 See Fig. A21.

The pump draws the products of the burning of the gas through the apparatus. A liquid collects in the bottom of the U tube and this can be identified as water by adding it to anhydrous cobalt(II) chloride (turns from blue to pink) and by measuring its boiling point (100°C).

The limewater quickly turns cloudy showing the presence of carbon dioxide.

If the experiment is repeated without lighting the Bunsen burner, little or no liquid will collect in the U tube and the limewater will take a long time to turn a little cloudy.

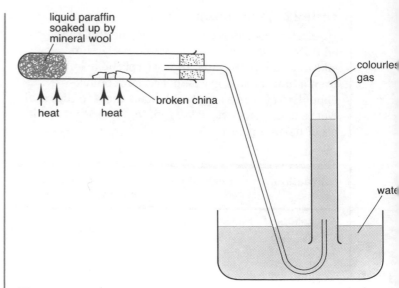

Fig. A20

Unit 23 Coal

2 (a) Ethyne (acetylene) is used in oxyacetylene welding and cutting metals. A mixture of ethyne and oxygen burns with a very high temperature flame. Ethyne is also used to produce chloroethene (vinyl chloride) which is used to make polychloroethene (polyvinyl chloride PVC)

(b) calcium oxide + coke → calcium carbide + carbon monoxide

$CaO(s) + 3C(s) \rightarrow CaC_2(s) + CO(g)$

calcium carbide + water → ethyne + calcium hydroxide

$CaC_2(s) + 2H_2O(l) \rightarrow C_2H_2(g) + Ca(OH)_2(s)$

(c) (i) The biggest difference between polyacetylene and other plastics is its ability to conduct electricity. It is also unstable in air.

(ii) The advantage of polyacetylene batteries over lithium batteries used in cameras etc is that they are rechargeable. They are also very much lighter and can be moulded into different shapes.

(iii) Lead is about 26 times heavier than an equal volume of polyacetylene.

(iv) The main disadvantage of polyacetylene is that it is unstable in air. This would not be a problem in a battery which could be completely sealed.

3 (i) The weighing after 5 minutes was less than after 10 or 15 minutes. This is because all the water had not been driven off after 5 minutes. The constant weight after 10 and 15 minutes shows that all the water has now been lost.

(ii) Mass of coal used = 61.25 g − 54.30 g = 6.95 g

(iii) Mass of water lost = 61.25 g − 60.60 g = 0.65 g

(iv) Percentage of water $= \dfrac{0.65}{6.95} \times 100 = 9.35\%$

4 Weigh an empty crucible. Reweigh the crucible containing a small piece of coal. Heat the crucible strongly in the air until the coal appears to have burned completely. When the crucible is cool reweigh it. Reheat the crucible for five minutes, cool and reweigh. Repeat the heating until a constant weight is obtained.

Percentage ash $= \dfrac{\text{mass of ash}}{\text{mass of coal}} \times 100$

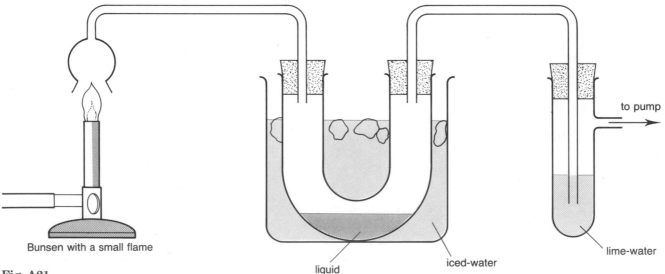

Fig. A21

Glossary

The following words may be met during your Chemistry lessons.

A

Absolute temperature There is a minimum temperature below which it will never be possible to cool anything. This is called **absolute zero** and is $-273°C$. This is the starting point for the **Kelvin** or absolute temperature scale: e.g. $0°C$ is the same as $273K$ on the absolute temperature scale.

Acid A substance that dissolves in water to form a solution with a pH below 7. An acid contains hydrogen which can be replaced by a metal to form a salt. The three mineral acids are sulphuric acid H_2SO_4, hydrochloric acid HCl and nitric acid HNO_3.

Alcohol An alcohol is an organic compound containing an OH group. A common alcohol is ethanol C_2H_5OH.

Alkali A base that dissolves in water to form a solution with a pH above 7. Alkalis are neutralized by acids to form salts. Common alkalis include sodium hydroxide $NaOH$, potassium hydroxide KOH and calcium hydroxide $Ca(OH)_2$.

Alkali metal A metal in group I of the Periodic Table. Common alkali metals include lithium, sodium and potassium.

Alkaline earth metal A metal in group II of the Periodic Table. Common alkaline earth metals include calcium and magnesium.

Alkane A family of hydrocarbons with a general formula C_nH_{2n+2}. The simplest alkane is methane CH_4. This is the main ingredient of natural gas.

Alkene A family of hydrocarbons with a general formula C_nH_{2n}. The simplest alkene is ethene C_2H_4. This is a most important chemical in industry.

Allotropy When an element can exist in two or more forms in the same physical state, it is said to show allotropy. The different forms are called **allotropes.** Diamond and graphite are two solid allotropes of carbon. Different allotropes exist because of different arrangements of atoms.

Alloy A metal made by mixing two or more metals together e.g. brass is an alloy of copper and zinc.

Amalgam Many metals form alloys when mixed with mercury. These alloys are called amalgams. The mixture used to fill teeth is an amalgam.

Amorphous Without definite or regular shape.

Analysis Finding out the elements present in a substance is called **qualitative analysis.** **Quantitative analysis** is finding out how much of each element is present.

Anhydride An anhydride (sometimes called an acid anhydride) is an oxide of a non-metal which dissolves in water to form an acid. Carbon dioxide is an anhydride, dissolving in water to form carbonic acid.

Anhydrous A substance without water. Often used to describe salts which have lost water of crystallization.

Anion A negatively charged ion which moves towards the anode during electrolysis e.g. Cl^-.

Anode A positively charged electrode in electrolysis.

Aqueous solution A solution made by dissolving a substance in water. The solvent in an aqueous solution is always water.

Atom The smallest part of an element that can exist.

Atomic number The atomic number is the number of protons in the nucleus of an atom. It is equal to the number of electrons in the atom. The elements in the Periodic Table are arranged in order of atomic number.

B

Base A substance which reacts with an acid to form a salt and water only. Metal oxides are bases. A base which is soluble in water forms an alkaline solution.

Battery A battery is a source of electricity. A carbon-zinc battery is the type of battery used in a torch. The battery in a car is a lead-acid battery which stores electricity. It can be re-charged.

Boiling When a liquid turns rapidly to its vapour at a fixed temperature called the **boiling point**. The boiling point of a liquid varies with pressure. The lower the pressure the lower the boiling point.

C

Calorimeter Apparatus used for measuring heat.

Carbohydrates Compounds of carbon, hydrogen and oxygen. The number of hydrogen atoms in each molecule is twice the number of oxygen atoms. These compounds are energy foods e.g. glucose $C_6H_{12}O_6$.

Catalyst A substance which alters the rate of a chemical reaction but is not used up in the reaction.

Cathode The negatively charged electrode in electrolysis.

Cation positively charged ion which moves towards the cathode in electrolysis e.g. H^+.

Chemical change A change which results in the formation of new substances. A chemical reaction is not easily reversed.

Chromatography A way of separating mixtures, especially of coloured substances, by letting them spread across filter paper or through a powder.

Combination The joining together of atoms of different elements to form a compound (see **synthesis**).

Combustion Burning is a combination of a substance with oxygen. Combustion is another word for **burning**.

Compound A substance formed by joining atoms of different elements together. The properties of a compound are different from the elements that make it up. The proportions of the different elements in a particular compound are fixed.

Condensation When a vapour turns to a liquid on cooling. Heat is given out during this change. Condensation is the opposite of evaporation.

Conductor A conductor will allow electricity to pass through it (electrical conductor) or heat to pass through it (heat conductor). Metals are good conductors of heat and electricity. Carbon, in the form of graphite, is a good electrical conductor but a poor heat conductor.

Corrosion Corrosion is the wearing away of the surface of a metal by chemical attack. The rusting of iron is an example of corrosion. Rusting of iron is an example of corrosion. Rusting requires the presence of oxygen and water.

Cracking Cracking is the breaking down of long hydrocarbon molecules with heat and/or a catalyst to produce short hydrocarbon molecules. The short molecules are much easier to sell, especially for making plastics.

Crystal A piece of a substance that has a definite regular shape. Crystals of the same substance have the same shape. Slow **crystallization** will produce larger crystals.

D

Decomposition A chemical reaction that results in the breaking down of substances into simpler ones. This is often brought about by heating, when it is called **thermal decomposition**.

Dehydration A reaction where water (or the elements of water – hydrogen and oxygen) are removed. Dehydration of ethanol produces ethene. The substance which brings about this reaction e.g. concentrated sulphuric acid, is called the **dehydrating agent**.

Density The mass of a particular volume of a substance. It is expressed as kg/m^3 or g/cm^3.

Detergent A detergent is a cleaning agent. There are two main types of detergent – soaps and soapless detergents.

Diffusion This is the spreading out of a substance to fill all of the available space. Diffusion takes place quickly with gases and liquids.

Dissolving When a substance is added to water it can disappear from view when stirred. This disappearance is called dissolving. The substance is still there and can be recovered by evaporation.

Distillation A way of purifying a liquid or obtaining the solvent from a solution. The liquid is vaporized and the vapour condensed to reform the liquid. The condensed liquid is called the **distillate**.

E

Electrode The conducting rod or plate which carries electricity in and out of an electrolyte during electrolysis. Graphite and platinum are good unreactive or inert electrodes.

Electrolysis The passing of a direct electric current (d.c.) through an electrolyte, dissolved in water or in the molten state, resulting in the splitting up of the electrolyte at the electrodes. Lead bromide, for example, is split up into lead (formed at the negative electrode) and bromine (formed at the positive electrode).

Electrolyte A chemical compound which, in aqueous solution or when molten, conducts electricity and is split up by it. Acids, bases, alkalis and salts are all electrolytes.

Element A single pure substance that cannot be split up into anything simpler.

Endothermic reaction A reaction which takes in heat.

Environment The surroundings in which we and other animals and plants live. A person who studies the environment may be called an **environmentalist**.

Enzyme An enzyme is a protein which acts as a biological catalyst. Certain enzymes only work with certain reactions. The action of an enzyme is best under certain temperature and pH conditions. Enzymes are part of the growing subject of **biotechnology.**

Evaporation The process by which a liquid changes to its vapour. This happens at a temperature below its boiling point but is fastest when the liquid is boiling.

Exothermic reaction A reaction that gives out heat e.g. the burning of coal. A reaction which takes in heat is called an **endothermic reaction**.

Extraction The removal of one thing from a group of other things e.g. separating iron from iron ore.

F

Fermentation Enzymes in yeast convert glucose into ethanol and carbon dioxide. This process can be used to dispose of waste sugars in industry.

Filtrate The liquid that comes through the filter paper during filtration.

Filtration (or filtering). A method of separating a solid from a liquid. The solid is 'trapped' on the filter paper and the liquid runs through.

Flammable Describes a substance, e.g. petrol, that catches fire easily.

Fractional distillation A method of separating a mixture of different liquids that mix together. The process depends upon the different boiling points of the liquids. The liquid with the lowest boiling point boils off first and is condensed. As the temperature is raised, liquids with higher boiling points distil over.

Freezing When a liquid changes to a solid. It will do this at the **freezing point**. A pure substance will have a definite freezing point.

Fuel A substance that burns easily to produce heat and light. A **fossil fuel** is present in the earth in only limited amounts and cannot be readily replaced, e.g. coal, petroleum.

Funnel A piece of glass or plastic apparatus used for filtering. A **Buchner funnel** is a particular type of funnel usually made of china. It produces quicker filtration because the filtrate is sucked through the filter paper.

G

Giant structure This is a crystal structure in which all of the particles are strongly linked together by a network of bonds extending through the crystal, e.g. diamond.

Group Vertical column in the Periodic Table. Elements in the same group have similar chemical properties.

H

Halogen An element in group VII of the Periodic Table. The word halogen means 'salt producer'. Common halogens are chlorine, bromine and iodine.

Homologous series The name given to a family of organic compounds, e.g. alkanes.

Hydrated Contains water.

Hydrocarbon Compounds made up from the elements hydrogen and carbon only.

Hydrolysis The splitting up of a compound with water.

I

Immiscible Two liquids that do not mix are said to be immiscible, e.g. oil and water.

Indicator A chemical that can distinguish between an alkali and an acid by changing colour e.g. litmus is red in acids and blue in alkalis.

Insoluble Describes a substance that will not dissolve in a particular solvent.

Insulator A substance which does not conduct electricity e.g. rubber or plastic. Insulators may be called **non-conductors**.

Ion A positively or negatively charged particle formed when an atom or group of atoms lose or gain electrons.

Ion exchange A process in which ions are taken from water and replaced by others. In an ion exchange column used to soften hard water, calcium and magnesium ions are removed from the water and replaced by sodium ions.

M

Malleable Metals are very malleable as they can be beaten into thin sheets or different shapes.

Melt A solid changes to a liquid at the **melting point**.

Metal An element that is shiny, conducts heat and electricity, can be beaten into thin sheets (malleable) or drawn into wires (**ductile**) is probably a metal. Metals usually have high melting points and boiling points and high densities. Metals burn in oxygen to form neutral or alkaline oxides.

Mineral A naturally occurring substance of which rocks are made.

Mixture A substance made by just mixing other substances together. The substances can easily be separated again.

Molecule The smallest part of an element or compound that can exist on its own. A molecule usually consists of a small number of atoms joined together.

N

Neutralization A reaction where an acid is cancelled out by a base or alkali.

Non-aqueous solution Solution where the solvent is not water e.g. iodine dissolved in hexane.

O

Oxidation This is a reaction where a substance gains oxygen or loses hydrogen.

Oxidizing agent An oxidizing agent, e.g. concentrated sulphuric acid, oxidizes another substance. It is itself reduced.

P

Period A horizontal row in the Periodic Table.

pH A measure of the acidity or alkalinity of a solution. The scale is from 0 to 14. Numbers less than 7 represent acids; the smaller the number the stronger the acid. Numbers greater than 7 represent alkalis; the larger the number the stronger the alkali. pH 7 is neutral.

Pollution The presence in the environment of substances which are harmful to living things.

Polymer A long chain molecule built up of a number of smaller units, called **monomers**, joined together by a process called **polymerization**. Polymers are often called plastics, e.g. poly(ethene) is a polymer made up from ethene molecules linked together.

Precipitate An insoluble substance formed in a chemical reaction. This usually causes a cloudiness to appear in the liquid and eventually the solid sinks to the bottom. The precipitate can be removed by filtering or centrifuging.

Product A substance formed in a chemical reaction.

Properties A description of a substance and how it behaves. **Physical properties** include density and melting point. **Chemical properties** describe chemical changes.

Pure substance A single substance that contains nothing apart from the substance itself. Pure substances have definite melting and boiling points.

R

Reactant A chemical substance which takes part in a chemical reaction.

Redox reaction A reaction where both oxidation and reduction take place.

Reduction Reduction is the opposite of oxidation. This is a reaction where oxygen is lost or hydrogen is gained. A **reducing agent**, e.g. carbon monoxide, reduces another substance. It is itself oxidized.

Residue The insoluble substance left on a filter paper during filtration.

Reversible reaction A reversible reaction is a reaction which can go either forwards or backwards depending upon the conditions. A reversible reaction will include the sign $\rightleftharpoons$ in the equation.

S

Salt A substance which is formed as a product of a neutralization reaction. A salt is the product obtained when hydrogen in an acid is replaced by a metal.

Saturated compound A saturated compound is a compound which contains only single bonds e.g. methane CH_4.

Saturated solution A solution in which no more of the solute will dissolve providing the temperature remains unchanged.

Semi-conductor Some substances, e.g. silicon, have a very slight ability to conduct electricity. They are called semi-conductors and are used to make microchips.

Solubility The number of grams of a solute that will dissolve in 100g of solvent at a particular temperature.

Solute The substance that dissolves in a solvent to form a solution.

Solvent The liquid in which a solute dissolves.

Spectroscopy The study of the light coming from a substance. Helium was first discovered by examining light from the sun. Helium must be present on the sun.

Sublimation When a solid changes straight from a gas to a solid **or** solid to a gas, missing out the liquid. The solid collected is called the **sublimate**.

Surface tension This is a measure of the attraction between molecules at the surface of a liquid. Water has a high surface tension.

Suspension A mixture of a liquid and an insoluble substance where the insoluble substance does not sink to the bottom but stays evenly divided throughout the liquid.

Synthesis The formation of a compound from the elements that make it up. This is usually accompanied by a loss of energy.

T

Titration A method of investigating the volumes of solution that react together.

Transition metal A block of metals between the two parts of the main block in the Periodic Table. Transition metals are usually dense metals much less reactive than alkali metals.

V

Vapour A vapour is a gas that will condense to a liquid on cooling to room temperature.

Viscous A viscous liquid is thick and 'treacle-like'. It is difficult to pour.

Volatile Describes a liquid which is easily turned to a vapour, e.g. petrol.

W

Water of crystallization A definite amount of water bound up in the crystal, e.g. $CuSO_4.5H_2O$.